MOTOR
MATTERS

THE IMPORTANCE OF DEVELOPING MOTOR SKILLS
IN OUR AUTISTIC SON

Written by Emma Eppard
Edited by Carla Morris

Cover and interior design by Pancho Eppard

ISBN: 9798637305889

TABLE OF CONTENTS

Disclaimer: This book reflects our family's journey, my understanding of RPM, and how it has worked for us. For a fuller discussion of RPM, please read Soma Mukhopadhyay's books.

Dedication: This book is dedicated in thanks to Carol Childs, Bec Mar, Lenae Crandall, Soma Mukhopadhyay, and to all who have been part of Team Philip.

A huge thanks to Carla Morris, Liz Fajardo, Sarah Churchill, Brittany Staley, and Glenn Kummerow.

INTRODUCTION

Receiving your child's diagnosis of autism is hard. It's the curveball that catches you unaware and the flood of emotions that leaves you breathless. It's the moment when everything you imagined for your child's development turns upside down. At least, that was my experience more than seven years ago when our son was diagnosed with autism. The diagnosis put our family on a journey of ups and downs in search of ways to meet his special needs. At times, responding to the challenge took all we had to give and more. It introduced us to a community of helpers and a network of friends who faced similar challenges. It exposed our weaknesses, but it exposed strengths, too. Remarkably, we discovered beauty, joy, and the wonder of unconditional love along the way.

We also discovered an approach to motor skill development that changed our world for the better. It gave us tools that proved effective even when our son's limited verbal skills posed challenge after challenge. This book is about that discovery.

Children who are nonverbal or limited in verbal skills can learn and will learn given the right support, discipline, and perseverance. This book assumes you are interested not so much in wishing for a miracle, as in coming alongside your child who struggles with motor challenges.

Our children deserve the good that life has to offer, including education, communication with others, independence, socialization, fitness, and a sense of belonging. All of these require motor skills. Motor development is golden for nonverbal children and children with limited verbal skills. It enriches their experiences and expands their options. For them to make gains, however, we, their advocates, must help them tackle skill development with fervor and dedication. It takes Olympians tens of thousands of hours to achieve their goals; we must be the Olympians of motor skill development for our children. This is our family's story of what worked for us, and how daily dedicated development of our sons' motor skills turned merely surviving to thriving.

CHAPTER 1

OUR STORY

Another rainy Saturday, and everyone in our family lazily mills around in pajamas enjoying the slow pace. We clear the breakfast dishes, break out the word game Mad Libs and set up cardholders. Laughter soon erupts at the goofy stories that unfold. Our oldest, Phil, sits next to me, thoroughly engaged. Five years earlier, I could not have predicted this scenario and all the ways our family would learn and grow together. I could not have predicted the joy we would know working hard to overcome unwanted challenges and pressing on to being better persons. I could not have predicted the deep satisfying appreciation we would cultivate for relationships or the stunning results of merely planting, tending and growing our garden of knowledge and skills daily. Five years ago, I never would have imagined that the boy who sat by my side reading cards in his pajamas now and taking his turn in round after round of a game, would be the catalyst of all this goodness.

O ur oldest son, Phil, was born in 2008. Like all new parents, we faced a steep learning curve. We adored him. I left my career as a teacher to stay home with him. I was thrilled to pour my love, heart, and soul into this tiny new person.

Phil's first two years were riddled with surgery, ear infections, and respiratory problems. At the age of two, he was verbal, but his skills were limited, and he did not seem to progress. At the age of two-and-a-half, Phil was evaluated by a speech therapist. It was the first time I had heard the word "autism" in relation to my child. One of my dearest friends accompanied me to evaluation. I will always remember what she said afterward: "He is the same boy you loved before this news and the same boy you will continue to love."

I felt at such a loss. Before the evaluation, I thought that if I taught and modeled enthusiastically, his speech would develop, and his repetitive behaviors would cease. After the evaluation, it saddened me that I had wasted time, not knowing how to teach him effectively. For the next several nights, I lay awake thinking, how could this be? How was I going to help Phil? What would his future hold? I felt sad and fearful.

For months, I found myself caught afresh with fear and sadness that our firstborn would likely not play little league baseball or participate in the school play. These thoughts brought me to tears daily. Though my emotions felt raw and close to the surface, I was somewhat able to gain perspective. Phil's evaluation gave me something to work with. It told me where I would focus my research to help him be his best.

Still, I vacillated between positivity and fear. I asked my mom to come and stay with us for a while, as I tried to ground myself. The support I received from my husband and mom during this time was a lifeline. Knowing we were in this together regardless of Phil's prognosis and that we would all love him unconditionally and strive for him to have the fullest life possible gave me a glimmer of hope. I researched autism therapies day and night. Just after Phil's third birthday, we settled on The Son-Rise Program sponsored by the Autism Treatment Center of America.

We attended all of the one-week training sessions Son-Rise offered and built a strong play therapy program at home with the help of volunteers and friends who comprised the close community in which we live. The foundational part of The Son-Rise Program changed our beliefs and attitudes toward our child. This change was instrumental in healing my heart and soul over the next three years. Each session delved more deeply into the psychology of beliefs. I came to understand that though my son was autistic, I was able to *choose* my response to his diagnosis. I could choose to love and teach, or I could choose to disconnect and wallow. I felt empowered as I practiced choosing my beliefs and channeling helpful emotions and energy toward engaging my son. This mentality of choosing my beliefs put me where I needed to be to fight and give my son every opportunity to succeed.

After three-and-a-half years in The Son-Rise Program, Phil was six-and-a-half years old. His eye contact had normalized, and his speech improved some. His interactions continued to increase through intensive one-on-one time in a play therapy room that a host of volunteers helped to staff. Many wonderful people entered our lives and shared our joy as Phil made each and every gain. In lots of ways, we found it to be a fulfilling, loving, and kind approach, but it lacked on the academic front. Phil was getting to the age where I was concerned that he would fall behind academically if I could not find a way to teach him. I did not want this void to compound his challenges with speech.

A dear Son-Rise mom shared information with me about the Rapid Prompting Method (RPM) for helping autistic children learn and grow. She was kind enough to share a video of her daughter doing RPM and spent time with me via Skype, explaining how RPM worked. I am forever grateful for that conversation; it compelled me to know more. She recommended I read two books: *Ido in Autismland* (Sharon Kedar, 2012) and *Understanding Autism Through Rapid Prompting Method* (Soma Mukhopadhyay, 2008). So began my RPM journey. In the fall of 2014, I looked for an RPM provider and booked some sessions to help me more fully grasp this method. Philip was six years old.

My paradigm began to shift when I witnessed an RPM provider speaking to Phil as if Phil were cognitively normal. Prior to this, I had mistakenly thought Phil only comprehended what he could say or point to. I did not understand that the motor to his mouth and body did not cooperate with his thinking brain. I watched the provider use a letter board* to draw responses from Philip and teach him. I cried. My whole world shattered. Through gross underestimation and ignorance, I had unknowingly limited the world I presented to my son and in turn limited his growth.

It took a couple of days for me to reconstruct my paradigm. I now believe and know that my son is capable of learning anything. Does he learn in the same way neurotypical kids learn? No. But he can learn, and he does learn!

Over the last four years, I have immersed myself in the world of RPM. In April 2016, I attended Soma's one week training in Austin, Texas. Now that I have read Soma's books, consulted with providers, taken my son to Soma, and frequently hosted workshops, I am continuing on a path to success for Phil.

When we began RPM in earnest, Phil was six-and-a-half years old. He was not potty trained, could not self-dress, could barely self-feed, and exercised no independent skills. We had exposed him to simple stories, colors, and numbers, but his academics were sorely lacking; I simply did not know any better. Helping Phil master academic lessons became my priority.

---

* a laminated sheet with alphabet letters grouped by rows into A-I, J-R, and S-Z

I am sure that after looking in on the first six months of my attempts to implement RPM lessons, an outsider would have deemed them a complete failure, but they weren't. I committed to undertaking two RPM lessons daily. At first, this translated into Phil throwing all the materials across the floor, flipping the table a dozen times, and leaving me crying in the bathroom. Still, I remembered that I had seen a provider succeed with the method. I was sure Phil was learning despite my botched efforts. It was just going to take more time for me to catch on. I had to be creative. I learned to enrich our lessons with drawing, building, and writing, using only paper and scotch tape as the method calls for. The daily practice was important for me to hone my skills as a teacher and for Phil to grow skilled in spelling on the letter board and in learning academics.

I began to equate my learning RPM techniques with playing a beautiful piano concerto. It was going to take intense practice and time for me to be the teacher Phil needed. Once I could play the piece perfectly from a technical sense, I would still need to learn how to finesse my artistic sensitivity and musicality. Each day I tucked in and gave it another go. It has been quite the journey, and I am still growing. I remain sorely lacking in natural aptitude for learning and understanding RPM techniques. I required and still require LOTS of practice to be the teacher my son needs me to be for him to grow.

RPM academic lessons only required 20-30 minutes twice daily in our homeschool day. This gave us time to add lessons that developed Phil's motor skills—skills that contributed to a fully functional life. I created lessons based on my understanding of Soma's blue book *Developing Motor Skills for Autism Using Rapid Prompting Method: Steps to Improving Motor Function* (Outskirts Press, 2014). Developing motor skills seemed to come more naturally to me than developing academic skills. Phil craved development in this area, too, as motor skills increased his independence. So, our daily schedule eventually included RPM lessons in academics, self-care, chores, hobbies, fitness, and reading.

Starting was a challenge; there was so much to teach. As a momma with three kids, I knew that addressing the initial motor skills listed would make my life easier. Daily, for a minute or two, I focused on teaching Phil how to self-dress and put on his shoes and jacket. Within six months he mastered these. Leaving the house with an infant, a five-year-old, and a seven-year-old now became possible! Thus, began our journey into motor skills for self-care. Then the wheels began turning. What other motor skills could Phil learn that might dramatically improve his life? I needed to buckle down and think these through. A plan emerged.

With intensity, discipline, drive and the help of friends, Phil and I have worked relentlessly each day on a plethora of motor skills. For my own personal organization, I aimed at four categories: self-care, chores, hobbies, and fitness. We started with mainly self-care skills, as these offered Phil the dignity many autistic kids do not experience, especially those who cannot enunciate for themselves. It took a full year for Phil to learn to tie his shoes. I cried so much the day he did it! It was not how long we had worked on it that got to me; it was the look on his face when he did it, beaming with sincere pride over mastering something that was previously so difficult. Seeing that look solidified in me the importance of teaching him additional motor skills. Our children need to feel that sense of pride. It is such a beautiful thing to work hard toward something and to know that your hard work paid off.

Phil worked next on making his bed and folding his laundry. These took nine months. None of the skills Phil has learned have come quickly. We are all about daily practice for a minute or two. And yes, we even learn and practice on the hard days, the sleepy days, the "I just want to curl up and read days"—*every* day.

Phil's self-esteem is through the roof now. He loves his ability to contribute to meeting his own needs, to being a part of our family community, and to having hobbies he can enjoy with his friends and family. His quality of life has gone from poor to wonderful. He experiences pride in himself and in his accomplishments. Also, my life as his momma has improved. He does not need me for everything, and in fact, of my three children, he is my most helpful and independent.

I learned many lessons taking the bullheaded approach. Primarily, I learned about the RPM community of parents and providers who are eager to help. Consider reaching out to experienced others any time small bumps arise in your RPM journey. Do not be like me and frustrate both yourself and your child. Other mommas and I want your journey to be easier than ours. We want to support you as you grow. Traveling with experienced others is an easier approach than taking the path of a lone ranger.

Though hard work eventually pays off, I also learned that it is best to work smarter, too. Combining hard work with a healthy dose of consultation with a provider and seeking advice from those further along the journey is the best plan. Although our second workshop with a provider left me better equipped, I still fumbled often. I added video consults and began hosting a provider every three months to help improve my skills in a more fruitful fashion. Teaching with RPM has many components. These include making a lesson plan, implementing the lesson, and reflecting on what could be done differently next time. It takes time to get good at each one of these, let alone all three. But, trust me, it's worth it!

Presently, in 2018, my son is potty trained, self-dresses, makes his bed, folds his laundry, empties the dishwasher, lays the table, self-bathes, vacuums, sweeps, assembles puzzles, colors pictures, assembles snap circuits, reads independently, and performs at grade level or a bit above in every subject. It has taken every bit of the last three-and-a-half years to get to this place. Phil engages in academic and motor lessons every single day. We exercise dedication and discipline, even on the hard days.

In the remainder of this book, I share the details of how we accomplished our motor goals. Yes, we have many more motor goals to meet, as Phil is only ten years old. Yet, I feel we have set a strong foundation on which to build the best possible future for Phil when we, his parents, are no longer here on this earth. Truth be told, it takes every ounce of my conviction, determination, grit, and persistence to stick at it. It takes discipline that, for me, is not innate.

I have learned that conviction and planning are not enough. Implementing the plan is essential. That means waking each day, intent on putting that plan into action. Like wedding vows, it takes daily commitment to make implementation a priority for better or worse, in sickness and in health. Many days I wake wanting a break, wanting to throw in the towel, or wanting to have a "normal" life; but that is not reality.

Reality for me is that I am a mother. Embracing that role has profoundly changed and shaped me. As mother, I want my children to be the best versions of themselves possible, and I will do all I can to support their development. This determination turns daily rigor into joyful action.

Perhaps an unwanted diagnosis has put your family on a similar path. Perhaps you and your child are just beginning your journey. I hope that some part of this book helps you as you teach and guide your child to realize his or her fullest potential.

CHAPTER 2

KNOW YOUR WHY

Philanthropy is on my son's mind. He tells me that he wants to help others. He already helps us around the house, emptying the dishwasher, vacuuming, sweeping, clearing the table. "Why not?" I think. "Why not affirm his desire to give, not just receive? Why not guide his development? Can he learn to mow a lawn? Can he learn to wash a car or rake leaves? I once decided to be the best mom I could be with the information at hand. That commitment has carried us far. Now he tells me that he desires to do for others. Just as we have shared joy in learning about dung beetles, volcano structure, weaving yarns and playing games—why not pursue skills that open doors to helping others? My heart is full with joy over the possibilities.

I am a person of strong conviction. For me to commit to working on something daily for an extended period of time, I need a solid reason and an answer to the question, "Why do this?" After all, the time it takes me to learn a new teaching technique and implement it with Phil is considerable; therefore, the required commitment must be worth it.

I found a compelling reason for dedication to the task when I realized Phil is cognitively intact and harbors the same wants and needs as any other person. Like all humans, he desires independence, socialization, and belonging. Once I understood the big picture encompassed far more than just education and communication and that motor skills were key to unlocking treasures in other areas, then helping Phil develop motor skills was clearly worth it.

Think about the time you use motor skills daily to unlock treasures. For about 50% of your day, you use motor skills in academics or work, 20% in self-care, 10% in chores, 10% in hobbies, and 10% in relaxation. As champions for our children's wellbeing, we want our children to develop motor skills in these areas, too. Nonverbal or limited verbal children need help learning how to use the key of motor skills to unlock treasures. They need someone to envision for them the possibilities of what can happen when a skill is developed; they need someone to identify a related goal, create a plan to achieve the goal, and guide them through practice to reach it. As Phil's mother, I choose to work with him on developing the motor skills he needs to be the best he can be in each area.

If I do not invest and provide Phil the opportunity to develop skills that help him succeed at life, what will his quality of life be once I am gone? I strive for him to have a complete life. As a very good friend of mine observed, I am fighting for the man Phil will be someday.

How can anyone accomplish such a bold endeavor? It starts with goals and a plan to achieve those goals. I began our journey with an extensive list of desired skills but settled on five motor skills to get started. In all honesty, the particular five I chose does not matter, but they were skills that would make my life easier and give Phil a sense of contributing to his independence. Twice daily for a minute or two, I guided Phil to zip his jacket, put on or take off his shoes, fold his laundry, loom, and empty the dishwasher. This first set of motor skills took over nine months to master.

Please keep in mind, there is no ideal timeline, just persistence. Each child is different and will require different amounts of time. The daily discipline is most important. There is no miracle, just hard work and the belief that it will come together whenever it comes together. My plan was and still is to stick with each task until mastery. I think of mastery as Phil being able to do a task without prompts. He has mastered a task when he initiates and follows through when needed. Also, each day I encourage him and stand by him, knowing that learning motor skills is hard. Having clear goals helps us move forward.

On this road to improved motor ability, we will not know if we have arrived if we do not identify a destination. Goals are the written destination, the "what" that we want to accomplish. I prioritize goals by their importance to me, plus the skills I feel Phil needs to be his best self. When it comes to identifying and prioritizing goals, it helps me to have a clear picture of my purpose, my "why," or my "mission" in mind. Capturing my mission in a succinct statement that I can reference often keeps me on track. This mission statement is the filter through which I sift all possible activities and skills and determine which ones to pursue.

Just as I crave a full life for myself, I desire for Phil to be well rounded. This includes gathering with friends and family, taking on chores, caring for self, fitness, and pursuing hobbies. To top it off, well roundedness includes preparation for some kind of eventual employment. My mission statement reflects these aims.

To help you brainstorm what is important to you in order to construct your own mission statement, here are some questions for you to consider.

1. What quality of life do I envision for my child?

2. Why is it important for me to make development of my child's motor skills a priority?

3. How much of an average person's life do I think requires motor skills?

4. How many of the activities that fill my child's life require motor skills?

5. What motor skills does my child need for self-care now? What skills will my child need for self-care as an adult?

6. What motor skills does my child need to master in order to function in the space where we currently live?

7. What motor skills will give my child more opportunities? How will these skills facilitate those opportunities?

8. What motor skills does my child need to thrive socially?

9. What motor skills does my child need to someday be employed?

10. What goal related to motor skill development do I envision my child achieving this year? In two years? In five years? In ten years?

Once you have thought through these questions and brainstormed responses, it is time to put your thoughts and beliefs into a mission statement. Your mission statement should capture what you imagine applies best for your child and you. Below are additional steps to help you write a useful and effective mission statement that suits your family. Your mission statement will be personal and fit your lifestyle.

After much thought, my current mission statement looks like this:

> Because I desire for Phil a life filled with independence, socialization, and belonging within our family and community, I commit to educate Phil daily both in academics and in the discipline of motor skills, which will give him greater self-esteem and confidence. This requires perseverance and consistency on my part, but I will work faithfully to give my son the fullest life he can have. I will encourage and nurture him with a positive attitude and give him constructive feedback when necessary.

Once you have finished creating your mission statement, it is time to start thinking about specific goals. Identifying both long-term and short-term goals is important. Long-term goals give you the bigger picture of where you want to arrive in the end. Short-term goals identify all the little steps it takes to reach a long-term goal. For example, a long-term grocery shopping goal for my son may be for him to shop independently, with me five paces behind. A short-term goal might be for him to push a cart and put a few groceries in it.

In the long run, I want Phil to need the least amount of assistance possible in his day-to-day living. What does "least amount of assistance" look like? I can't predict, but I do know that growth is possible. As parents, we can choose to do nothing, or choose to dabble at teaching skills now and then. Then again, we can choose to give growth our all and count every small gain as a win. Many persons have conquered odds requiring herculean effort; why can't we be among those people?

My son's success addressing motor challenges and growing more independent has come, not with occasional practice, but with Olympic-like discipline and hard work. My mission statement gives me the clarity I need to continue to identify priorities and set long and short-term goals for which we strive.

Our current goals include grocery shopping for short lists of items, using the fewest prompts possible; independent face washing; standing patiently in line; tennis; swimming; and working 150 piece puzzles. In the next two years, we plan to move Phil toward mowing and raking for our family and others. Phil would also like to develop skills he can use to help others, like washing cars and light gardening. It is important that he takes part in setting his motor goals and impacting his community at large. His communication via RPM has given him tools to express his fullest desires including philanthropy; he wants to give, not just receive.

Leaning on your mission statement puts your priorities into perspective and leads to concrete goals. My priority was improved quality of life for both Phil and me. I understood that Phil's independence directly correlated to his self-esteem and to my responsibilities to help him grow. Starting with what would give both of us the independence we valued appealed to me. Because it appealed to me, I knew I was likely to persist in teaching.

Understanding how we use motor skills throughout the day helped me choose goals. Remember, only about half of our day consists of education or employment. This leaves plenty of time for other pursuits. For our children, these pursuits can contribute to their self-development, household chores or leisure activities —all of which require learned skills. Consider how children spend their days, at school or home. How do they develop the motor skills they need to thrive?

I strongly believe in education and communication. However, I feel that people often downplay the importance of motor skills and the role motor skills play in giving our children the best possible life. For many years, Phil was up in the mornings just running circles around our house. He was not able to contribute and could not even sit in a chair and self-feed. At age ten, after three years of intentional practice in developing motor skills, he is able to wake and dress himself, pour drinks for his siblings, set the table and get the dishwasher emptied while I make breakfast. His sense of belonging and contribution has shifted immensely, and our whole family has benefited having him on the team instead of on the sidelines. And don't we want our children to join us in life as a part of our community at home and contributing to the greater community around us?

Some questions to consider for self-reflection:

Are you as a parent ready to look at why you may or may not want to teach your child motor skills?

Which category of motor skills is most important to you: independence, socialization or belonging?

What three motor skills do you plan to tackle upon completing this book? Appendix A lists some possibilities.

Consider your current lifestyle and situation. To what degree are you committed to skill development right now? What might you release to make teaching motor skills a priority?

CHAPTER 3

GETTING YOUR HEAD IN THE GAME

I grew up in Bolivia, South America. When I came to the U.S. for college at the age of 17, I had no idea how difficult navigating a new culture, new freedom, and a new level of education would be. Initially I felt like a flailing fish out of water. But I engaged in this new world, and the emotional storms gradually ushered in a welcome calm. Surely Phil feels like this when he watches his peers exercise motor skills with ease. He may be out of his element initially, but I've seen him overcome. The world has gradually become an easier place for him; his willingness to grow has ushered in a measure of calm. My struggle transitioning from one culture to another is an integral part of who I am. It colors my appreciation for life and how I see the world. Phil's struggles to transition will mold him, too; his growth and victories will be all the sweeter.

I t is human nature to avoid what is difficult. We do not look for opportunities to fail; instead, we tend to favor revisiting areas where we do well. When it comes to learning motor skills, our children do not have that luxury. They have to face what is hard straight on, and not just sometimes, but daily. From the moment they wake up to the moment they go to bed, they are aware of their motor limitations. Our job, as champions for their growth, is to face what's hard with them daily. Initially, you might not be the best at teaching motor skills; you, too, will face what's hard. You can grow that skill in the same way that you want your child to grow.

As a champion for Phil's growth, I set the attitude, the perspective, and the discipline needed to give Phil every opportunity to succeed. When we take on a new motor task, I can count on Phil resisting with fervor for the first six weeks. His running away, loud vocalization, and minimal cooperation often express his natural resistance to face difficult things. I know enrichment and joy await Phil on the other side of tackling what's hard. As a champion for his growth, it is imperative that I remain patient, encouraging, and consistent with practicing skills. I have to think about the effort it takes Phil to learn, how frustrating it can be, and then support him lovingly. At the same time, I do not quit because he does not look happy. I do not stop because he does not seem to like it. I do not let my ten-year-old boy dictate his life, because he cannot foresee what is best for his future.

In the book *How to Talk So Kids Will Listen & Listen So Kids Will Talk* (Scribner 2012), authors Adele Faber and Elaine Mazlish detail the importance of responding to and validating the emotion you think your child is experiencing. Emotions are good and real to your child in any moment. As parents, we often want to guide, direct, and give advice instead of acknowledging what our child feels. Even though Phil cannot speak functionally, when he starts to tense or retreat from a motor activity, I find that affirming what I perceive his emotion to be helps. Just a quick labeling like, "You seem frustrated," lets him know I relate. With children who have limited or no verbal ability, we inevitably miss the mark sometimes and label the emotion wrong. However, in my experience with Phil, he knows that I am trying to empathize. The care and respect he feels help him continue.

In her book *Mindset* (Ballentine Books, 2007), Carol Dweck discusses two differing perspectives that have helped me understand and successfully model language that helps Phil be successful: the fixed mindset and the growth mindset. The fixed mindset holds that each moment defines you. If you do well at a task, you are amazing. However, if you fail at the next task, you are horrible. This limiting mindset puts our children on an emotional roller coaster. If they can do something, then they are good; if they can't, then they aren't. We never want our children with differing abilities to think their worth lies in performance. We are not training a pet to do tricks, but rather, we are raising up our children to be independent and capable. If each moment defines Phil, his self-esteem is in for a daily beating.

The growth mindset focuses on the journey instead of the outcome. From this perspective, it is exciting to learn something new, and—as with many new pursuits—there will be stumbling along the way. Each glitch is a reflection of growth. Mistakes do not exist; failed attempts at a skill, just like successful attempts, are part of learning. Phil's motor growth has been and will continue to be a long journey. It is not enough for me to praise each tiny step, because I know that significant gaps occur between each step. Rather, I choose to embrace the joy of trying daily, knowing that even when there is no apparent progress, Phil is still learning and giving it a shot. I have learned that progress will come if we persist.

Practicing motor skills daily is like placing individual grains of sand into the beginnings of a sandcastle. A single grain seems insignificant, but each grain works together with the others to make the structure. Each day when you work on motor skills, you add another grain of sand to the castle. Yes, this work can be tedious because there is no expediting, cheating, or shortcut; only doing. There is nothing miraculous about Phil's motor development. We are simply consistent. In time, we have seen his capabilities shift; in times to come, we expect them to shift even more.

Discipline is not innate; we develop it. Did you know that it takes over 30 days to develop a habit? Habits can be good or bad. For instance, if I decided to take a break and avoid working on motor tasks with Phil, in a short time, I will form a habit, and he will stay exactly where he is in his abilities. If I decide, however, to focus on one motor skill daily, I am forming a habit of honing his motor skills. This choice gives hope for greater personal growth and development. Deciding to spend 15 minutes each day focused on motor skills forms a habit that spans over 90 hours of opportunity and learning in one year. If starting with 15 minutes seems too hard for you, start small with five minutes to get the ball rolling. Once you are consistent with five minutes, increase to ten minutes. The attention span of most children and adults is 15 to 29 minutes; one 15 minute motor session daily can change the game.

About two years ago, at a conference on autism, one woman's encouragement brought the importance of motor development into perspective for me. Her severely autistic son was in his fifties. I sensed others listening to her catch their breath as I did when she said, "Please keep in mind, whatever your children cannot do for themselves, someone else will have to do for them… and it will not always be you." This hit me hard. If Phil cannot bathe himself, someone will have to bathe him. I value his dignity. This requires me to step up and create discipline in my life for his benefit.

I have seen that the hard work is worth it. Disciplined habits can be cultivated. Consistency breeds growth and really does change things. Those grains of sand really do make a castle. Start building yours. Begin with a grain each day and watch how your castle emerges as you and your child embrace opportunities to change together. A better quality of life awaits both of you.

CHAPTER 4

UNDERSTANDING AND USING PROMPTS

It is early morning. I hear Phil waking up, and I wait, pausing to see if he will come out of his room without hearing my voice. I hear the click of the doorknob turning and the familiar sound of Philip entering the bathroom. I trot down the hallway into the kitchen. Within a few minutes he appears, completely dressed. He grabs his audiobook CD, puts it in the CD player and turns it on. Finding a comfortable corner of the couch he settles in and enjoys the story. In just a few minutes, he has successfully and independently exercised a host of motor skills to start his day.

P hil, like others who are nonverbal or limited in verbal skills, has trouble with initiating activities. He struggles to get his body started to execute a task, and he struggles to stop his body from executing a task. He can want his body to obey his mind, but he needs help to get his muscles to actually follow through. Prompts help him follow through. Prompts are actions taken by the parent of caregiver to help the child to initiate a task and carry it to completion.

Many parents express concern that their children will become incapable of doing an activity without a specific prompt. I believe prompt dependency happens when prompts are used incorrectly.

Prompt dependency occurs when the parent or caregiver overuses a single prompt. Perhaps the same word is used each time to trigger a child's muscle response to start a task. In time, without that specific prompt, the child will not start the task. For example, when Phil needs to wash his hands, I may prompt him by saying, "soap." Over time, Phil will be unable to function at the sink without the prompt, "soap." Overusing a word prompt or overusing one type of prompt is problematic. When we rely on only one prompt, we do not achieve independent, reliable skills; rather, we elicit a trained response. This begs the question, what happens when the trainer is no longer available to speak commands?

The most effective way to avoid prompt dependence is to use a myriad of prompts to stimulate action. According to Soma, there are four different prompt categories: auditory, visual, tactile, and kinesthetic. She writes extensively about these in her book *Understanding Autism Through Rapid Prompting Method* (Outskirts Press, 2009). Following, is a brief description of each.

Auditory prompts involve any kind of sound, words or nonsense words; even a grunt or "hmmm" qualifies. Auditory prompts vary in volume from the tiniest whisper to the loudest yell. They can be melodic, chanted, spoken, or delivered in different accents or pitches. Sound sensitive students sometimes need extra quiet, even whispered prompts to initiate a motor movement. Phil often enjoys funny voices and random words delivered via song.

Visual prompts are those a child sees. They include gestures, building something, drawing something, or any movement in the child's visual field. Effective use of visual prompts requires focus. And, while peripheral vision enhances perception, visual prompts benefit most from direct focus. When we want a child to see what we are doing or discussing, and she looks off and to the right, we need to put the item we want her to see in her field of vision (where her eyes are looking). Phil has worked extensively on focus. He used to fatigue quickly, sustaining focus only for a minute or two, but now he is able to use his eyes for up to 20 minutes at a time. Visual tolerance is a skill that can improve but it takes practice. Visual proficiency is vital for reading, self-dressing, and many hobbies.

Tactile prompts engage touch. When I ask Phil to start folding his laundry and he is unable to move, I tap his hand to help him get started. When his muscles are sore, I prompt a good stretch by placing stickers on his knees and ankles. They cue him to alternate between touching his knees and then ankles. If we are in the grocery store and he pauses despite me calling him, I touch his shoulder briefly to get him moving again. If I want him to pick up a grocery bag, I may brush the handle against his hand to initiate his grasp.

Parents or caregivers use kinesthetic prompts when they manipulate the child's body to help it get started. To initiate drawing, I sometimes put my hand over Phil's. To remind him how to catch a ball, I place his hands out in front of him, palms up. To demonstrate the motion of peddling a bike, I move his feet in a circular motion. Some kinesthetic prompts can be slight. When Phil dresses, for instance, I might push his foot just barely to start him getting his pants on. When he eats, I slightly move his hand in a better position to grasp a cup.

The combination of prompts and motor modeling has taken Phil from no skills to many skills. Motor modeling is the technique of placing the caregiver's or parent's hand over the student's hand to demonstrate a skill two to three times, then immediately having the student try the same skill independently. I usually use a gesture or verbal prompt to get Phil started, but also know to vary the prompts we use daily to keep from dependency. Ultimately, we want all prompts to diminish over time. Beginning to teach a new motor skill, I sometimes use motor modeling, auditory prompts, and visual prompts. I want to use only as many prompts as Phil needs. Just as prompts can become a habit for the student, they can become a habit for the caregiver or parent.

How do you know the number of prompts your child needs to accomplish a task? A little experimentation helps. Sometimes I vary the prompts and then drop one or two to see Phil's response. When Phil cannot do the task, it tells me that my prompts are not sufficiently supporting him. He may need more prompts or different prompts. If he is doing something well with two prompts, I might try removing one. Each day, I play with removing prompts, because I can always immediately add a word, gesture, or touch if needed. My goal is for Phil to feel well supported. Phil and I are a team; we learn alongside each other.

Two Dimensional Versus Three Dimensional

Rapid Prompting Method (RPM) is a teaching technique that empowers the student to communicate thoughts and reason through open learning channels in an instant of learning. The learning channels can be auditory, visual, kinesthetic, or tactile.

RPM can take the form of formal educational lessons that use choices and a letter board. The parent or caregiver teaches, and the child responds by touching a written choice provided or pointing to letters on an alphabet stencil or paper. Some RPM academic lessons and motor lessons use a letter board; some do not. RPM often goes well beyond the boards to incorporate all motor activities. For more details on the learning channels, refer to Soma's book *Understanding Autism Through Rapid Prompting Method* (Outskirts Press, 2008).

When it comes to teaching motor skills, it helps to understand the difference between 2D and 3D learning environments. When we point to letters on a letter board or objects in a picture, we work in a 2D environment. In 2D, the letter board or picture is in the child's performance field, where the child's hands work functionally to respond to a lesson. Working in a 3D setting involves using the hands to point to objects on a tabletop, grasp and release, or retrieve an item. For example, I might lay out a $1 bill, a $10 bill, and a $20 bill on the table and have Phil spell on the letter board what is on the table. This is 2D learning. When I ask Phil to pass me the $1 bill, the learning shifts to include a 3D motor task. Without practice, Phil will likely retrieve the wrong bill.

For children to function appropriately in the 3D world, it helps that they practice skills in the 2D world first. Working in 2D builds confidence and prepares them to tackle the harder 3D task, that is, manipulating their hands in accordance with their brains. This distinction between 2D and 3D is important. While I know Phil understands that I want him to choose the $1 bill, his understanding does not mean his hand can complete the task. One way to practice this is to place a picture of the bills at letter board level, point to the $1 on the picture, and then bridge from the 2D to 3D by pointing to the $1 bill on the tabletop. Once Phil points to both of those correctly, he is better able to grasp the correct bill.

The motor skills we explore in the following chapters are divided into 2D and 3D examples. These examples and subsequent interpretations flow from my family's personal experience. They are anecdotal in that respect. I hope that our experience helps you better implement techniques to aid your child in developing new motor skills for improved self-esteem and greater success navigating life. Keep in mind, Soma has written extensively on the development of motor skills. We consider her a trusted authority on the best way to go about teaching skills.

CHAPTER 5

INDEPENDENCE

On a crispy fall afternoon the park seems the ideal place for my three kids to run off energy and get fresh air. We finish our snack, and I tell the children we will head to the park once all three brush their teeth and put on their shoes and jackets. They hurry to the bathroom while I quickly rinse dishes and tidy up the kitchen. I hear the sound of water running and electric toothbrushes whirring. The hubbub then moves to the front door in a scuffle of shoes and jackets. Within a minute or two, we are all are out the door and headed for the park. The children—including Philip—required no help from me as they prepared to leave the house. I sigh in thankfulness for this gargantuan victory.

Staring at the huge mountain of developmental needs that towered over Phil and me, I felt overwhelmed. According to developmental standards, my son at age six-and-one-half functioned close to the level of a neurotypical one-year-old. The most advanced skill he demonstrated was sucking through a straw. I didn't even know where to start. There seemed so much to do. How would I ever help him catch up with his peers?

To complicate this challenge, Phil was not my only child. I had two other children, a four-year-old and six-month-old, who also needed my attention. With so many people needing me, I was nowhere near able to get everything done in a day that I needed to. Independent self-help skills for Phil would relieve much of that. If Phil were more able to care for his own needs, the quality of life he experienced would improve, and the quality of life our family experienced as a whole would improve. I needed to carry that vision with me to the base of that towering mountain, section off a sliver of challenge and give it a try.

Which sliver? It helped me to imagine our usual day. For instance, think about your child's daily activities and the life skills those activities require. What are you doing for your child daily that would be helpful for him to learn? When you wake up, what is the first thing he needs you to do? Imagine if upon waking, he were able to do that task independently. Dream for a moment about him being able to take a shower with a few simple reminders, dress without help, or fold laundry alongside you.

Though Phil's success depended on me understanding motor modeling and how to use different prompts, teaching self-help skills posed a steep learning curve for me. I am still learning. Anytime he struggles is an opportunity for me to think about effective prompts that will help me support him. I share the details of my journey teaching self-help skills in this chapter. Again, it flows from my understanding of Soma's techniques as explained in her blue book, *Developing Motor Skills for Autism Using Rapid Prompting Method: Steps to Improving Motor Function* (Outskirts Press, 2014).

Two Dimensional Independent Motor Skills

You can teach the 2D of any motor skill and then transfer focus to 3D with just a minute or two of daily practice. Be sure not to frustrate your child, however. Phil and I found that brief practice (three to four minutes) daily or three times a week works well. He needs practice, but he must feel successful, not like his efforts are fruitless. Planning lessons that effectively develop motor skills is a challenge in part because you must always consider your child's self-esteem.

It can be tempting to repeat the same academic RPM lesson if your child is not successful transferring well to the 3D phase. Remember that if your child has an open learning channel and you have presented the material, he or she has heard you. If your child has auditory or visual tolerance, you can simply tell or show your child the steps on paper and read the steps together. Having the child spell the same lesson is not needed; repetition can lead to frustration. Just remember that your child hears and sees often. You can tap auditory and visual learning channels without using the letter board.

Why do our children get frustrated? The same reason that we do. They are not successful, or they perceive disrespect. Think about your own life. Do you appreciate it when people only tell you the same story repeatedly? Of course not. Such repetition insults your intelligence. Our children's intelligence deserves respect, too.

Washing Hair

I approached hair washing by drawing a picture or printing a picture of Phil and putting it in his visual field. I pointed to the head on the picture. Then I had him point to the head on the picture. I then put a piece of tape on Phil's arm and his head, preparing him for an instruction. With choices narrowed down to his arm or head, I asked him to touch his head. If needed, I took his hand and touched his head two to three times, then requested him to do it (motor modeling). We practiced this daily until Phil could touch his head with the fewest prompts, for example, just a verbal prompt "head" or me gesturing to my head, a visual prompt.

Next we moved to lathering, or the circular motion on the head. I would refer to a paper on a clipboard at letter board level and take his hand showing him how to make a rubbing circular motion on the paper. He is able to see it at letter board level, whereas on his head he is not able to see. From there, I took his hand and motor modeled the circular motion on his head. We practiced the circular motion on his head daily over time. I tapped different areas of his head to show him all the spots that needed the circular motion, and motor modeled each of those. We practiced until he could do the motion all over his head with the fewest prompts.

Phil still struggles to stop squeezing the inverted shampoo bottle. It helped when we gave him a travel size shampoo bottle; we're still working on the fine points of this skill. I put the shampoo and bar soap on the tabletop and, at letter board level, drew a picture of both, as they laid on table. I asked him to point to the shampoo bottle on the drawing, then point to it on the table. I provided prompts as needed. Once he could point to the bottle of shampoo, I asked him to grab it.

Grabbing and releasing are two separate motor skills. Just because Phil can grab the shampoo bottle, does not mean he can release it and put it back on the table. He also has to practice releasing the bottle on different pieces of tape (visual prompt). So, for a minute or two each day we practiced grabbing and releasing a variety of objects, as this is something we all do several times a day in different settings. Phil's control over his hands has improved with practice, but it still varies from day to day. This reminds me that the trajectory for our children's skills is not a straight line, just as development in my life and yours has not followed arrow straight paths. The prospect for growth improves when a guide meets us where we are at in any given moment and supports us as we move forward from there.

Turning over a shampoo bottle and squeezing the shampoo into the opposite hand requires both sides of the brain, as each of the hands performs a different action. This is called differentiation. To teach this skill, I begin with pointing to the bottle, picking it up, and opening the lid. I motor model with auditory prompts to begin with and then pull back varying my prompts each day. Again, we do this daily for a about a minute. Then we add the step of squeezing, if needed, to get enough shampoo for the job. Your child can practice this with an empty bottle if you prefer avoiding the mess. Please note, when using shampoo your child might need to build tolerance to the sensation of the shampoo on her hand.

Once the shampoo is squeezed into the opposing hand, this hand then needs to get to the top of the head. Motor model as needed along with auditory prompts. Then proceed with what has already been practiced, the circular motion all over, lathering, and rinsing. When your child is able to tolerate these steps with your support, move to using all these skills in the shower. Keep in mind, the change in location and the sensory experience of the water adds many different elements. For the first several times, it may feel like your child has forgotten what you have taught. Stick with it, motor model as needed, and be supportive in your prompts. It will come together, but first it will seem like a few steps backward before you step forward again. Changes in the environment impact our children; they do not generalize like you and I generalize. For more information on this read discussions of accommodation and assimilation in Soma's red book *Understanding Autism Through Rapid Prompting Method* (Outskirts Press, 2008).

Folding Clothes

Beginning to fold clothes in 2D requires paper and tape. Tear a shirt shape out of paper and place tape on one sleeve. At letter board level, have your child point to the piece of tape. Then add a piece of tape to the center of the shirt. Have her point to that piece of tape. Together, take the sleeve tape to meet the center tape. Undo it and execute it together again. Then allow her to try independently. Practicing with paper is helpful as it is not floppy like fabric and can be folded in the child's visual field, where his or her eyes are working.

With Phil, I aimed for practice folding on the tabletop with the fewest prompts, eventually removing even the tape prompt. Then, we practiced once on paper and once on the real shirt, gradually reducing use of the paper shirt after a few times. Do this a little each day; there is no set timeline for how long mastery will take. Children like Phil struggle with controlling their hands. Also, changing from a paper shirt to a fabric shirt will add extra elements of challenge. Each transition takes time, so be patient and consistent.

Putting On a Pullover Shirt

You can introduce the topic of putting on a shirt in several ways. A brief RPM lesson laying out the steps of putting on a shirt works well, or talking the process out, or making a list in your child's visual field and reading it aloud. From a 2D perspective, refer to a printout of your child's body on an 8.5" x 11" paper. A great way to begin is by pointing through the steps on the picture, then on your child's actual person. Hold the photo in his visual field. Start by having him point to the head on the picture. Then ask him to point to his own head. If this is challenging, tap his head and another body part to narrow it down to two choices. Next, practice pointing to each hand on the picture. Mirror this action by pointing to your child's hands. Do this a time or two each day until he is able to touch the points on his body with only an auditory (verbal or sound) or visual (gesture) prompt.

Next, introduce the actual shirt and place it on the bed with the head hole ready to be put on. Have your child point to the head hole; then encourage your child to grab it. If needed, motor model (your hand over your child's hand) two to three times and then have your child immediately try. Move to putting the head through the shirt, followed by the arms. Motor model these steps. It is important encourage and offer as many prompts as needed for your child to feel successful. Again, a little practice daily goes a long way over time and keeps frustration to a minimum.

Wiping One's Bottom

The action of wiping involves grabbing, wiping, and releasing. Remember that your child executes the wiping and releasing without being able to see the actions. Walk your child through the steps, explaining them verbally or writing them in the student's visual field and reading them aloud. You only need to do this a time or two as your child can learn through seeing or hearing the instructions.

In the bathroom, have your child sit on the toilet with the seat cover down. Wherever the toilet paper is located, draw a picture of where it is, and anything else that might be grabbed nearby. Point to the picture of the toilet paper, and then point to the actual toilet paper roll. This mirroring from 2D to 3D helps children have more control of their hands as they transition to only 3D. Grabbing the end of the toilet paper, pulling, and holding constitute three different motor tasks. Motor model how to grab, pull, and hold. Support the child with any prompts necessary and know this is something that will require practice over time.

The wiping action should be taught prior to trying it on one's bottom. This can be practiced using toilet paper or tissues on the tabletop. Motor model wiping with your hand over your child's hand, moving your hand up and down two to three times. Then, immediately give your child an opportunity to try the motion independently. Practicing the wiping action on the tabletop is a start. Your child will still need to practice this on her bottom. She can practice while still clothed, sitting on the toilet seat cover. Again, a little practice every day goes far, and there is no ideal timeline; success happens when it happens.

Brushing Teeth

It took us well over two years of intentional teaching with Phil to master teeth brushing. Still, from time to time, he reverts to chewing on his toothbrush. When that happens, I add prompts or bring motor modeling back for a period. As with all children, motor skills can become bad habits or haphazard and need correction. From a 2D standpoint, there are many items the hands have to grab, release, and hold. Draw a picture or take a photo of the location of your child's toothbrush and toothpaste. Have your child to point to these 2D references, followed by pointing in the 3D. This "mirroring" paves the way for success.

Once she is able to point out and grab the toothpaste, motor model (that is, your hand over her hand) removing the lid and squeezing the toothpaste onto a stationary toothbrush. Motor model this action two to three times, then have her immediately try. Phil and I found that having the toothbrush laying on the sink was easier than holding both the toothbrush and the toothpaste in order to apply the toothpaste. Also, we practiced squeezing the tube with the lid still on so he could feel the impact of the pressure he applied. You can buy travel size toothpaste tubes to begin with, as they contain less toothpaste and are easier for some children to hold. Practice this in the context of teeth brushing twice per day.

When it came to brushing teeth, Phil and I found motor modeling helped. I would brush his front teeth twice with my hand over his hand, then he tried it a few times. We then moved on to the back top left, back bottom left, back top right, back bottom right, and bottom front teeth. I led the process by motor modeling with Phil taking his independent turn. We continue to brush his teeth in the same order each time as this helps develop Phil's muscle memory. Some of the challenges we ran into were Phil chewing the toothbrush, laughing, or balking at the sense of the toothbrush in his mouth. However, we stuck with it, and brushing teeth continues to improve. Phil often goes a few months brushing effectively and slowly forms some bad habits, which I try to address quickly. When this happens, we motor model again for a period with verbal prompts or gestures. In time, we wean back from the prompts, and they fade.

Examples of Varying Prompts in a 3D Setting

Below is a sample day-by-day break down of lessons in independent skills that we followed and the prompts I used each day to help Phil succeed. As you will see, each day is different. There are what feel like steps forward and also steps backward. Our journey shows a back and forth that ultimately moves forward, just not in a nice neat line.

Think about your journey as you learned long division in elementary math. There were probably days when the numbers seemed to cooperate, and other days where it felt like you were at war. Overall, though, in time, you moved decidedly forward. With that in mind, my hope is that you see the importance of meeting your child where he or she is at each day. Some days the elements will seems to cooperate for your child; other days a battle ensues. Overall, though, in time, your child will move forward.

Washing Hair

Sunday
While showering today, Phil needed verbal prompts to grab the shampoo, squirt it, and lather his head. I said, "grab it," "squirt it," and "circles" to get his hands moving.

Monday
Today I gave Phil verbal prompts to grab the shampoo, but he was not responsive. This auditory prompt did not work. I chose to squirt some shampoo on the top of his head as a tactile prompt. Then I used a visual prompt—pointing to the spot on my head—to help him initiate lather. He washed his hair with these two prompts.

Tuesday
Today, showering was a little different. I verbally prompted him to wash his hair, and he grabbed and squirted the shampoo. He did not initiate the lathering step, however. I tried a visual prompt by pointing to my head, but he was not

paying visual attention. I decided to try a kinesthetic prompt by placing his hand on his head and moving his hand in a circular motion for a second. He then initiated the lather.

Wednesday
As Phil was showering today, he initiated taking the shampoo and squirting it on his head. He washed his hair all by himself without me saying a thing. I know, however, that just because he washed his hair today without any prompts doesn't mean that it will happen tomorrow. I make a mental note to meet Phil where he is at each day.

Thursday
Today Phil washed his hair on his own without me giving him directions on what to do next. The only prompt I delivered was for him to wash his hair.

Friday
I told Phil (auditory prompt) that he needed to shower and get ready for bed. He got in the shower. I was surprised to see him washing his hair when I checked on him. As a mother, these moments of joy and pride overwhelm my heart. Hard work really does pay off.

Saturday
Today's journey toward independent showing started with what seemed like a setback. Phil needed auditory and visual prompts to begin washing his hair. He picked up the bottle of shampoo, but then stopped like he had forgotten what comes next. Supporting him with an auditory prompt, I said, "Pour it in your hand." He did so, but went to rinse it immediately instead of lather. I stuck my head in the shower and demonstrated on my own head what he needed to do, a visual prompt. Once I did that, he was able to lather and rinse.

Folding Clothes

Sunday
Folding a shirt involves several steps and can be challenging. At first, I demonstrated this task on a table, appealing to Phil's visual learning channel. I started with the visual prompt of folding the arm in on the left while saying "side in," an auditory prompt. I unfolded it and said "side in" for him to do the same. I continued this pattern of demonstrating with auditory prompts followed by him trying immediately for both sides of the shirt. I said "bottom up" for folding the hem of the shirt to the shoulders. Phil watched me and repeated my actions, helped by auditory prompts. This day, they seemed to meet his needs for support.

Monday
We started again with a shirt on the table; Phil even helped me straighten it
out. His hands did not sync with his brain to do the next step. I used a tactile
prompt. I touched his arm and grabbed the part of the shirt that needed to
be folded, verbally prompting him, "Side in." At my prompts, he was able to
fold the other side of the shirt. When it came to folding the shirt's hem to the
shoulder, I placed a piece of tape on the top of the shirt. I combined this tactile
prompt with the auditory prompt "bottom up" to get him to bring the hem up to
the shoulder. The combination of auditory and tactile prompts brought success.

Tuesday
I started with the auditory prompt "help me" to get him to work with me to
straighten the shirt on the table. This time I told him to place his shirt flat on
the table. I then placed tape on every spot that I wanted him to fold the shirt
to. I placed tape on his left arm and told him to fold the left side of the shirt, so
the left side touched the tape. Then I touched his right arm and told him to fold
this side of the shirt in the same way. Once both sides of the shirt were folded,
I placed tape on the top of the shirt and touched his arm, directing him to fold
the shirt vertically in half. After what felt like several steps and a lot of work, we
achieved a folded shirt.

Wednesday
Using the verbal prompt "side in" and pointing to the left arm (a visual prompt),
I got Phil to fold the first half. I pointed to the right side with the verbal prompt
"side in." He was able to do that side also. I said, "bottom up." He completed
the task.

Thursday
Today, I wanted to try fewer prompts. I handed Phil one of his shirts and
proceeded to fold my own shirt across from him—a different visual prompt.
This prompt seemed sufficient to get him to complete the folding steps. Though
it worked this time, it does not mean it will work every time. Still, variation is
important.

Friday
To help Phil achieve greater independence, I try to vary the prompts we use
daily and use fewer of them. I aim for balance between success and challenge.
On this day, I gave him a shirt to spread out on the table. A soft whisper of
"side in" from me got him started folding. I encouraged him saying, "You've got
it"—a verbal prompt and affirmation. That kept him going.

Saturday
On this day, Phil objected to everything. When he has days like this I know that

getting him to do anything is a struggle. Still, I commenced folding shirts. Phil values belonging. Once he saw me folding my shirts, he was motivated to join in. When a part of the process proved challenging and he froze, I used verbal and tactile prompts to get him moving again. "Side in," I said, followed by touching his left arm to initiate the move. That seemed to help.

Putting On a Pullover Shirt

Sunday
I placed a shirt next to Phil and told him that we would start working on putting this on him. First, I showed him that the shirt has a front and a back. I also showed him the shirt's three holes where his arms and head go. I used verbal prompts today. Holding the shirt open, I said, "Head in." Once he had the shirt over his head, I pointed to his left arm while holding the left side of the shirt open and said, "Arm in." I did the same for the right. He inserted his arms. Last, I told him to pull down the shirt to make sure it laid flat on his body. I pointed to the bottom of the shirt and told him, "Pull it down." This mixture of gestures, visual prompts, and auditory prompts supported him, and he completed the task.

Monday
Today I tried combining a visual and auditory prompt by pointing to the dresser drawer and saying, "Open it." Once Phil opened the drawer, I told him, "Grab one." He grabbed the top shirt. I said, "Close it." Phil placed the shirt on the bed. I held it up and pointed to the top opening where the head goes. He put his head through the opening. After he inserted his head through the hole, I pointed to each armhole one at a time, prompting him to insert an arm in each hole. He succeeded. As he accomplished each step, I encouraged him saying, "I believed that you could do it," and "I know you can."

Tuesday
Upon waking, I told Phil that he needed to open the dresser drawer and get a shirt out. I hoped that just using auditory prompts would work, but it didn't. I walked Phil to the dresser and pointed (visual prompt) to the drawer. I added a tactile prompt by tapping his arm and saying, "Open it." This got him to open the drawer, but I needed to point again for him to pick the shirt up. I needed him to close the drawer, so I pointed to the open drawer and said, "Close it." He did so. To get him to put the shirt on, I touched his head, and then I put my head through the shirt—a visual prompts—for him to see what I wanted him to do. Once he inserted his head through the shirt, I tried just tapping his right arm. Still, he didn't move. I used a visual prompt again by putting my arm through the armhole to demonstrate what he needed to do. After he inserted

his right arm, I hoped for a bit of cooperation from the other arm. I tried just tapping his left arm so that he would put it through the hole, and he did. This day, he required more support from me. I noticed he needed a variety of prompts, too.

Wednesday
Today I was a bit more creative with the way that we worked putting on the shirt. I tried saying, "Phil get a shirt out of the second drawer in your dresser." He went to the dresser, but opened the wrong drawer. I said, "Close. Just go down one." Together we counted the drawers starting from the top, and I told him, "When we get to two you can stop . . . one, two and stop." He stopped. He opened the drawer and grabbed a shirt without me saying anything. He then sat on the bed. I touched his head, pointed to the shirt, and said, "Head in." When it came to putting his arms through, I picked up a ball (visual prompt) and told him to grab the ball through the sleeve of the shirt. We did the same with his other arm. Using the visual prompt worked well.

Thursday
Phil and I were in different rooms. I called out an auditory prompt: "Phil, please grab a shirt from the second drawer and try to put it on." When I checked on him, he had already pulled the shirt over his head. Commending him for trying to do things on his own, I told him, "That's good. You've got it! Now finish." He stared at me and remained still, so I touched one arm at a time and gestured for him to put his arm through each hole. This combination of tactile and visual prompts brought success. This day, I used fewer auditory prompts, and he did most of the work. I commended him.

Friday
I called Phil over, and I pointed to the second drawer of his dresser for him to open it, a visual prompt. Then I pointed to a shirt on the top of the pile, gesturing for him to pick it up. He grabbed the shirt, but forgot to close the drawer. I reminded him, "Close it." He sat on his bed waiting for the next step. I tapped his head and pointed to the shirt, using tactile and visual prompts to get him started. Once his head was through the correct opening, he initiated putting his left arm through the left armhole. Then, he stalled. My gentle tap on his right arm and point to the right armhole got him moving again. Today tactile and visual prompts seemed to help the most.

Saturday
This day, I wanted to take a step back and see how Phil's body would respond. I stood farther away and used a verbal prompt. "Grab a shirt," I said. He got up and grabbed a shirt from his dresser. He began to walk away, however, leaving

the drawer open. I used a verbal prompt, "Close it." He turned around and pushed the drawer shut. He sat on his bed and put the shirt over his head, but then stopped. I reminded him "arm in" for each arm. He completed the task without me being right next to him.

Wiping One's Bottom

Sunday
Whenever a motor task is new to us, I use a lot of verbal and visual prompts. When Phil was done using the bathroom, I took that opportunity to teach him to wipe himself. Using visual prompts, I took the roll of toilet paper and demonstrated to him how to pull and then rip. I then handed the roll of paper to Phil so he could attempt to do the same on his own. I said, "Pull." When I saw he had enough, I said, "Stop." Then I said, "Rip." With a little bit of hand-over-hand help, he was able to manage the task. For wiping, I had him stand up so he could see his actions. Over my clothes, I demonstrated to him the motion that he needed to do to be able to wipe clean. I showed him how to reach under his bottom and then wipe back. This skill is tough, because Phil can't see his action. Still, visual modeling and encouraging him worked well together. Also, I checked his results and sometimes wiped one last time.

Monday
Phil yelled, "Mom!" As he finished using the bathroom I entered, letting him know that he was going to try to wipe himself again today. I pointed to the toilet paper and told him, "Pull, stop, and rip"—a combination of visual and auditory prompts. After he finished that part, I told him to stand up and wipe from the front to the back. Again I demonstrated the motion as a visual prompt. He took the paper and wiped himself.

Tuesday
Today I used a combination of tactile and visual prompts. I tapped Phil's hand and pointed to the toilet paper, indicating for him to get some paper. He wasn't looking at me, so in his line of sight, I motioned with my hands, showing he needed to pull, stop, and rip. Once he visually engaged, he got the paper, and I didn't have to use an auditory prompt. When it came to wiping, I tried holding a little piece of toilet paper on his back, right above his bottom. I told him, "Wipe from the front toward the back to reach the paper." This tactile prompt helped him wipe on his own.

Wednesday
While in the bathroom with Phil, I used visual and auditory prompts by pointing to the toilet paper and telling him to "pull." He grabbed the paper and

pulled without stopping. I said "stop" and "rip," which spurred him on. When it came to wiping, I demonstrated the movements on myself and said, "Wipe front to back." He completed the task with these prompts.

Thursday
It might seem repetitive, but when you encourage and support your child through the various steps, you instill confidence. Eventually he or she will do it independently. Helping Phil wipe himself today reassured me as a parent that practice pays off. I went into the bathroom when Phil called me and pointed to the toilet paper. He pulled, stopped, and ripped it off, independent of prompts. With toilet paper in hand, he seemed to freeze, so I said, "Wipe front to back." That was enough for him to initiate the movement of wiping.

Friday
On this day, several different prompts were necessary to support Phil. I pointed to the toilet paper for him to grab it, but nothing happened. I decided to combine tactile, visual and auditory prompts. I tapped his hand, pointed to the paper, and said, "Pull." Once he had grabbed some toilet paper, he just sat still. Using visual prompts, I demonstrated that he needed to stand up and wipe from front to back. This helped him complete the task.

Saturday
When Phil called me to help him in the bathroom, I opened the door and just used verbal prompts saying, "Pull, grab, and rip." I followed this with, "Wipe front to back." Today, these prompts were sufficient to achieve success.

Brushing Teeth

Sunday
Working on brushing Phil's teeth took lots of hand-over-hand movement. Starting off, I placed a toothbrush in his hand and told him, "Hold it." Placing the toothpaste tube in Phil's other hand, I said, "Squeeze gently." I was okay that a lot came out on his first try. I used a visual prompt and pointed to his mouth, followed by the verbal prompt, "Open." Once he opened his mouth, I placed my hand over his on the toothbrush and showed him the way that he needed to brush. I moved my hand over his hand and said, "Back and forth."

Monday
In the bathroom I pointed to the cabinet that the toothbrush was in and said, "Open it." He did. I pointed to his toothbrush saying, "Grab it." I did the same with the toothpaste. I had him hold the toothbrush in his non-dominant hand and use his dominant hand to squeeze. I prompted verbally, "Squeeze gently."

He squeezed a little too much. Still, I affirmed him and said that what he did was great. I reminded him to use just a little less the next time. Again, I motor modeled by placing the toothbrush in his dominant hand and brushing back and forth together two to three times. I then had him try independently while I gestured and said, "Back and forth."

Tuesday
Today, I wanted to make sure that I changed my prompts and attempted to support a little less. Using a visual prompt, I pointed to the cabinet and said, "Open." Once he had it open, I pointed to his toothbrush and said, "Grab it." I pointed to the toothpaste and before I said anything, he picked it up. Pointing to the top of the tube, I said, "Open it." He needed a bit of help when it came to twisting the top open. I placed my hand over his and helped him open it. I used a visual prompt by pointing to the toothbrush and showing him the squeezing motion to help him initiate applying toothpaste on his toothbrush. I told him to put the toothbrush in his mouth and go back and forth, then switch to the other side and go back and forth.

Wednesday
Verbal prompts worked on this day. I told Phil to open the cabinet and grab the blue toothbrush. "Twist it open," I said. "Squeeze the toothpaste out." Phil didn't get it on the first try, so I moved to help. He did not want my help though. I showed him the needed action by a making circular motion, gesturing, to loosen the cap. He tried several times on his own and finally got it. Again, I used visual prompts to aid him in brushing. I had him look at his face in the mirror, and I opened my mouth, saying, "Open." While continuing to have my mouth open, I used a tactile prompt by tapping his hand and said, "In." I then went back to visual prompting and used my own toothbrush. He looked at me while we both did the motions together.

Thursday
Today, at my visual prompt of pointing to the cabinet, Phil was able to open it and grab his toothbrush. He then closed the cabinet, so I reopened it and used a verbal prompt to have him take the toothpaste, too: "Grab it." I showed him, within his visual field, a twisting motion with my hands. I said, "Twist it open." I pointed to the toothbrush and toothpaste, indicating for him to place some toothpaste on the brush. Using a tactile prompt, I tapped the side of his cheek and said, "Open." I guided him, saying, "back and forth" and "front and back." When I wanted him to brush his front teeth, I said, "Smile and brush." He did.

Friday
I aimed to use verbal prompts only today. However, I was aware that I might

have to adjust and add prompts as needed. When we were in another room, I told Phil to go into the bathroom and brush his teeth. I hoped my verbal prompt would initiate his body. Once I heard the door close, I waited a minute and then checked on him. I saw him just standing in the bathroom. I used a tactile prompt and tapped his arm, combined with a visual prompt of pointing to the cabinet. Opening the cabinet helped him see the toothbrush, and he was able to grab it. Before he closed the cabinet, I said, "Toothpaste." I pointed to the top of the toothpaste tube and said, "Twist it open." I gestured to the toothbrush and toothpaste, making a squeezing motion. He started brushing at my prompts, "Back and forth . . . front and back."

Saturday
"Phil, please brush your teeth," I told him, pointing to the bathroom. Again, using visual prompts, I pointed to the cabinet, and he opened it. I pointed back and forth, alternating between the toothbrush and the toothpaste, so he would pick both of them up. This time I pointed to the toothbrush and said, "Toothpaste it." When he began to brush his teeth, I said, "Remember back and forth, and smile to get the front."

It Takes Time

Based on our experience and using my understanding of RPM principles, I can say that learning any independent self-help skill takes time. By "time" I do not mean a month or a year, but often several years. Desired results came when I stuck with it, varied the prompts, remained patient and respectful, and consistently guided Philip's practice a little every day. No miracle occurred, just hard work for a short period each day over time.

For example, when teaching Phil how to tie his shoes, I initially used motor modeling to show him how to cross the strings. I placed my hand over his hand two to tree times, immediately followed by his independent effort. We repeated this for one to two minutes each day until he could do it with only a verbal prompt. Then we moved to crossing the strings and pulling one string through, again with motor modeling, and eventually paring down to a verbal prompt. Then we moved to making loops or "bunny ears" until mastery, followed by wrapping the string around, pushing and pulling it through as needed. The process entailed many steps performed many times, but ultimately it all came together.

Looking back, I can see that putting skill development for tying shoes on a projected timeline for skill mastery would not have helped. How long would each step take? I had no idea, I just knew that I would support with the needed prompts and commit to intentional daily practice. It took a full year, but now

Phil is able to get his own shoes on when we leave the house. He values that piece of independence and knows he worked hard for it. I fully supported him and respected him throughout the process.

Of the elements that have shaped our skill development journey—modeling motor skills, varying prompts and demonstrating respect, perseverance, tolerance, and patience—tolerance for both Phil and me has been the most important. My ability to tolerate the daily teaching even on rough days was— and still often is—a work in progress. Also, Phil's tolerance with himself, his skills, and my teaching grew over time. When I think of all the amazing inventions and accomplishments gifted and determined contributors have accomplished throughout history, I am quite certain perseverance and tolerance played vital roles. When I think of the amazing accomplishments my son has achieved and will achieve, I am equally certain perseverance and tolerance are key. A "no quit" approach ultimately sets the stage for success.

CHAPTER 6

BELONGING

I wake up to the sound of the children stirring and soon make my way to the kitchen to start our day. In no time, from my place at the kitchen sink, I hear the floorboards creak as little feet come down the hall. Phil turns the corner first, fully dressed. He looks at me, and I return the look with a glance at the dishwasher. He walks over to it, opens the door and seamlessly empties its contents. The radio plays in the background; Philip's sister and brother appear. Nearby, I get breakfast going. This is a snapshot of us most mornings, "doing" life together.

The desire to belong is innately human. We want to be a part of something—a family, a community, or a group of some kind. When we contribute or fill a role within the group in some way, we feel like we belong. Our children have these same desires and aspirations to belong. They do not want to be on the sidelines; they do not want to be waited on or coddled, but to truly have a role all their own. Phil's sense of belonging was enriched when he acquired motor skills that allowed him to do chores; our family was enriched by his participation, too.

I remember begrudgingly doing the chores I was assigned as a child. I saw them as an intrusion on my will. Still, other family members valued my contribution and the results of my contribution. My pitching in brought a certain satisfaction. I suspected that pitching in would give Phil a sense of satisfaction, too. Phil did not take kindly to my idea of introducing chores. He was accustomed to waking up and roaming around, spinning whatever object he encountered. I meddled with his morning routine when I introduced emptying the dishwasher and laying the table. But, several months later, I saw a new Phil. He walked taller, prouder, and happier. He had changed for the better.

Two-dimensional Belonging Motor Skills

Motor skills associated with chores can be challenging because they require many different movements of the body in combination with syncing the eyes. You can move a glass, but if you don't look where you are going, it could smash into the counter instead of rest on top of it. Starting by teaching chores in a two-dimensional setting and bridging to a three-dimensional setting is pivotal for the child to develop hand-eye coordination. Like other motor skills, we exercised skills associated with chores in a two-dimensional setting before plunging into the added layer of the third dimension.

Talking through the steps of a chore or drawing the steps of a chore within your child's visual field is a great way to introduce a new skill. Use paper to point to or build objects and keep things in the letter board area of success. This will help you scaffold new motor skills and keep his confidence intact at the same time. Don't forget to prompt for success. You and your child are a team; if he struggles, add more prompts or motor model. Support him as needed. Remind him that you are in this together and that frustration is a normal part of learning something tough.

I started with vacuuming, as it is something that I do not enjoy and would love one of my children to take on. What chore do you wish your child would do? It took a year of hands-on work with Phil to teach him to vacuum. Now, looking back three years later, I am so thankful as I am reaping the benefits of that year's worth of teaching. Remember that when you develop motor skills associated with chores, you also invest in your child's feelings of belonging, and you lighten your own load, too. Be intentional now, and both you and your child will benefit in the long run.

Laying the Table

Participating in laying the table is a great way for a child to contribute to a family meal. It is a way for children to also contribute meaningfully to extended family gatherings or parties with friends. Begin by laying out a place setting on a tabletop and take a picture of the setting to print on a full sheet of paper. Alternately, you can draw a place setting on a full sheet of paper. Sitting in front of the table setting, hold up the picture at letter board level and have your child point to the fork in the picture. Next, point to the fork on the tabletop. Practice with each of the items, pointing on the picture first, then pointing to the corresponding item on the tabletop. Repeat this daily until the child can do this easily. Then have your child point to the items without the aid of the picture. If your child falters, bring the picture back to ease the transition as it is needed. We don't want to withhold help from our children, but rather we want to meet them where they are. This respects their self-esteem while continuing to move toward the goal of independent skills.

Once your child can point to each of the items without first pointing to the picture, it is time to start working on grabbing and releasing each of the items. Remember, grabbing and releasing are separate motor skills; practice is imperative. Ask your child to grab the fork and release it back into its spot. Or, use a piece of tape—a visual prompt—to mark a new spot. Have her practice moving the fork to where it needs to be. Once or twice daily, guide her practice of grabbing and releasing each utensil and the plate.

Next, put a plate and the utensils on the table in a pile. Your child will take items from the pile to set a place. Remember to prompt as needed, using tape or stickers and/or gestures as visual prompts. Use verbal encouragement as an auditory prompt, or tap your child's hands to help initiate—a tactile prompt. Also, motor model by taking your child's hands and moving an item to its location two to three times. Then, have your child immediately try independently. This will take practice. Equate it to learning a new violin piece; the finesse comes over time.

Sorting Silverware

All families use a fair amount of silverware each day, which ends up either in the drying rack or the dishwasher after a cycle is complete. Sorting and placing each piece of silverware in the drawer is a helpful skill in family life and potentially helpful in a work situation. To start, place a fork, knife, and spoon in the appropriate slots in a silverware drawer divider and place the divider on the tabletop. Take a photo or draw a picture of the silverware divider. Using the photo, have your child point to the fork on the picture and then point to the fork on the tabletop. Do this with each utensil. Then ask your child to point to the fork on the tabletop without using the photo first, transitioning from 2D to 3D. If this is a challenge, remember to provide more prompts to support your child's success—gestures, words, or tapping your child's hand to initiate movement. If needed, bring back the photo for reference and practice some more from that point.

When your child can point to each of the silverware spots with minimal prompts, place a fork outside the silverware divider and have your child point to it. Ask him to grab it and place it in the correct silverware slot. Motor model this new action, hand-over-hand two to three times; then let him immediately try independently. Provide prompts via gestures, words, or a rolled piece of tape (tactile prompt) on the fork slot. It is important to support him to be successful, so use as many prompts as needed at first, and gradually remove them in time.

Vacuuming

To begin, you might share a short traditional RPM lesson about the parts of the vacuum or vacuuming, or simply talk to your child about the process. If your child tends to be visual, write pertinent information in her visual field and read it aloud. When I initially planned how I would teach Phil to vacuum, I had only thought about the pushing and pulling movements that vacuuming required. Then I realized the process included many more steps, like unwinding the cord, inserting the plug in a socket, releasing the handle, and turning the vacuum on.

Start with taking a photo of the vacuum and pointing to the switch, cord, handle, and plug on the photo. Mirror these actions with the actual vacuum. From there, motor model each step starting with unwinding the cord two to three times then letting your child try independently. Support your child with gestures or verbal prompts as he unwinds the cord. Now teach plugging the vacuum into an outlet. Motor model this, hand-over-hand two to three times, and then have him immediately try independently, plugging in the vacuum.

Using a tape or sticker visual prompt, show him where to place a foot to push down the front of the vacuum and snap the handle out. Use your hand to guide his foot if needed, and repeat this action a couple of times. Then use prompts to encourage independent practice. Your child may only move his foot slightly, but this is something. In time, with practice, his foot will land where it needs to land. Every new movement and step your child accomplishes is important.

Work with your child to hold the handle of the vacuum cleaner and show the action of pushing and pulling two to three times. Let him immediately try it independently. Hover your hand nearby to catch the handle if needed, as safety is essential. Keep alternating between hand-over-hand and your child trying independently. Use other prompts as needed like gestures, words, or a gentle tap of the hand to keep him moving. Remember, starting and stopping pose real challenges for our children, so your prompts make all the difference in your child's initial ability to perform.

Once you've achieved the pushing and pulling motion with just a few prompts, the next step is making sure there is full floor coverage. I started with putting little pieces of colored yarn on the floor as a visual prompt and pointing to all the places that needed to be vacuumed. At times, I would stand in front of the vacuum and gesture. Other times I would use verbal prompts to encourage vacuuming up a piece of yarn. Eventually we worked on doing the perimeter, then lines all along the middle. Remember to vary your prompts. There will not always be obvious dirt to collect; but the visual prompt is a start.

Phil did not like vacuuming initially. He would cover his ears and move the vacuum at the same time. Over the course of several months, however, he grew more tolerant. Now, vacuuming is one of his favorite chores. I do have to make sure that he starts in a different room each time, or he develops some OCD habits about the order of his vacuuming—just a caution in case your child is like mine and tends to adhere too strongly to routines.

Clearing the Table

Growing in independence includes learning how to clean up after yourself. Our children want that same inclusion in being part of the family—not the feeling of always being waited on, but the feeling of contributing to the household as an active member. Many of us recall the simple chore of clearing plates from the dinner table. When it came to clearing his place, Phil did not trust his hands to act according to his thoughts. This made him anxious about carrying breakable items, but we worked through it.

Start with a photo or drawing of the place setting. Point to each of the utensils on the picture, then mirror this by pointing to each utensil on the tabletop. Motor model picking up each utensil and placing it on the plate, hand-over-hand two to three times. Have your child immediately try independently. Use words or gestures to support your child when trying independently. Once all the utensils are on the plate, motor model placing both hands on the edges of the plate to grab it. I reminded Phil that my hand would be under the plate if his hands faltered, and I also affirmed that it is fine if the plate drops or breaks. I also reminded him that carrying the plate would take practice, but if we do not practice our hands will not change.

Wiping the Table

When it comes to adopting new motor actions, it seems Phil's hands work best when he first practices at letter board level where his hands work functionally instead of impulsively. Introducing the wiping action on a clipboard at the location where he used the letter board provided a solid start to this functional movement for us. We practiced wiping in circles, up and down, and back and forth, with just his hand on the clipboard. Then I added a paper towel and continued to practice at letter board level, with the added element of holding a paper towel.

We practiced this briefly each day, then began to do it also on the tabletop. I guided him to wipe for three to five seconds on the clipboard, then three to five seconds on the tabletop. Then we removed the clipboard and wiped directly on the tabletop. When needed, I motor modeled, hand-over-hand two to three times. I then had Phil try independently. After we did well cleaning what was in front of us on the tabletop, I provided a visual prompt—a dot of soap at various spots on the table—and we aimed to wipe those. Again, I increased the prompts as needed for Phil to succeed in this new larger range of movement.

Examples of Varying Prompts in a 3D Setting

Some days when you wake up in the morning, you are ready to go; other days, you may be more sluggish. Your child is just like you. There are days when things seem to come together more easily, and there are days when everything feels like it's falling apart. Your goal is to provide the prompts your child needs each day to develop the motor skills you've identified as important. Prompting in a three-dimensional setting may vary from day to day. Following are challenges that we encountered as we developed skills related to chores and how we used prompts to navigate our way through those challenges to success.

Laying the Table

Monday
I brought Phil over to the silverware drawer and motor modeled grabbing the utensils, hand-over-hand two to three times. Then he immediately tried, grabbing a fork and knife. When he tried independently, I gave the verbal prompt of "grab it" and gestured toward each of the utensils. Once he had grabbed them, I guided him to the table and had him place them on two pieces of tape, a visual and tactile prompt. Then we retrieved a plate from the cupboard, where I reminded him that my hand was under it should his hands stop working. I gestured toward the table, and he placed the plate on the piece of tape marking its spot.

Tuesday
Opening the silverware drawer and pointing to the fork and knife—both visual prompts—I said "grab it" to get his hands to initiate selecting the utensils. Using both verbal and visual prompts, I gestured toward the table and said "over there" for him to head to the table. At the table, I requested he put them down, adding the visual prompt of pointing to the correct spot. I touched his back, a tactile prompt, to turn him back toward the cabinet to grab the plate. He opened the cabinet, but needed more support to complete the task. I motor modeled grabbing the plate with him. He took the plate to the table, helped by the verbal prompt of "over there." These prompt combinations aided his success.

Wednesday
I tapped his arm and pointed to the silverware drawer, a combination of tactile and visual prompts. He opened the drawer. I waited to see what he would do, and he seemed distracted until I said, "Grab them." He grabbed the fork and knife and turned toward the table. He placed the utensils down together, and I redirected by pointing to the two spots they belonged in, a visual prompt. He relocated them. I used the verbal prompt "plate" and he headed to the cabinet to grab it. However, on the way back, he fumbled the plate, and it fell on the floor. I quickly scooped it up and reassured him that I had forgotten to put my hand under it. I pointed out that I mess up too sometimes. He grabbed another plate, and I floated my hand under it while pointing to the table, a visual prompt. He placed it on top of the fork. I verbally prompted with "oops" and he corrected it.

Thursday
I used the verbal prompt "grab it", and pointed to the silverware drawer. He walked over, opened it, grabbed a fork and knife, and placed them on the counter. I pointed to the silverware, then to the table, and said, "Over there." He picked them up off the counter and took them to the table, laying them down backwards. I requested he look at the table, and I said, "Close, but let's switch them," an auditory prompt. He switched them. He independently headed to the cabinet, grabbed a plate, and placed it correctly on the table.

Friday
I opened the silverware drawer and verbally prompted him saying, "Grab it." His body was unresponsive, so I motor modeled, taking his hands in mine and grabbing a fork and knife twice. On the third time when I asked him to grab the utensils, he was able to grasp them, but he dropped them. I motor modeled again, and he was able to hold on to them. I waited, and he headed to the table on his own. He placed the fork and knife correctly. He appeared to freeze after that, so I tapped his shoulder and he immediately began walking toward the plate cabinet. He grabbed a plate, and set it on the counter. I pointed to it and gestured toward the table saying, "Over there." He took the plate to its proper location.

Saturday
I pointed to the silverware drawer, and he opened it to retrieve a fork and knife. He took them to the table. Then, he sat down in the chair. I verbally reminded him, "Grab a plate please." He remained seated. In his visual field, I pointed to the cabinet and said, "Plate please." This combination of prompts worked. He got up, grabbed a plate, and placed it on the counter. I tapped his shoulder; he picked up the plate and took it to its correct location at the table.

Sunday
Today, I tried saying, "Please lay the table, Phil." He got up and headed to the silverware drawer, opening it. He then took all the forks out and put them on the counter. I tapped his hand and said, "Grab one fork and one knife please." He did, and took them to the table. He set them down on the table together and walked to the plate cabinet. He grabbed a plate, took it to the table, and set it atop the fork and knife. I used a verbal and visual prompt, pointing and saying, "I don't think that's quite right." He looked down and moved the plate to its correct location. I gestured to the fork and knife, and he arranged them correctly.

Sorting Silverware

Monday
I called Phil over to the open dishwasher and pointed to the clean silverware, a visual prompt. I requested he grab the forks, an auditory prompt, and he started to grab all the utensils. I tapped his hand, a tactile prompt, and pointed out a few forks for him to gather. He collected a few in his hand. I then opened the silverware drawer and pointed to where they belonged, both visual prompts. He placed them in the drawer correctly, helped by the tactile, visual, and auditory prompts. I pointed him back to the dishwasher and used the same set of prompts for removing the knives. Phil succeeded.

Tuesday
Today I used an auditory and tactile prompt. I had put a rolled piece of tape on three forks in the dishwasher. I asked Phil to find the forks. I pointed to the drawer, a visual prompt, and he placed the forks in their space. To get him started on sorting the next utensil, I touched his shoulder and said, "Grab the knives." He grabbed them and placed them in the drawer with no further prompts.

Wednesday
I tapped his shoulder and asked him to put the forks in the drawer. This is a combination of tactile and auditory prompts to initiate his body. He started removing the forks, but became distracted. I gestured in his visual field, pointing to his hand and the drawer. He placed the forks in the correct spot. Returning

for the knives, he took out one and just stood still. I said, "Go ahead." He was able to grab the next one and place it in the drawer, too.

Thursday
Today I gestured, asked, and tapped him, but he did not seem to be able to get his body going. I motor modeled, hand-over-hand two to three times. Then, he immediately tried, grabbing the forks and putting them in the drawer. On the third attempt, he was able to do it with added verbal prompts of "grab it," and "find its spot." When it was time for the knives, I again motor modeled. That seemed to get him connected with his motor ability to complete the task.

Friday
I silently nodded at the dishwasher and he started removing the forks and placing them in the drawer. Once the forks were done, he began to walk away. A simple tap on the shoulder and point to the silverware got him back. He grabbed the knives and put them away.

Saturday
This time I put a rolled piece of tape on his hand and pointed to the dishwasher. The tactile prompt helped him find his hand and the gesture cued him to move in the right direction. He took the tape off his hand and grabbed the forks, placing them in the drawer. He started with the knives, but got distracted. I gently gave him the verbal prompt of "grab it and find its spot." He was able to complete the task.

Sunday
I requested, "Please put the silverware away." He grabbed the forks and placed them on the counter. I opened the silverware drawer and simply said, "Oops." This prompted him to put them in their spot. He looked at the knives, but did not grab them. I tapped his hand; he grabbed the knives and place them in the drawer. Providing prompts when Philip is stuck or when he makes a mistake helps to keep him going.

Vacuuming

Sunday
Today, I told Phil that he would start a new task to help around the house: vacuuming. Since it was the first time, I walked him through all the steps needed. We discussed where to find the vacuum, how to unwind the cord and insert the plug into the socket, how to turn on the vacuum, and how to vacuum. I taught each step by motor modeling, hand-over-hand two to three times. He immediately tried independently.

Monday

Today, we focused on vacuuming a whole room, practicing the motion all over the carpet. We walked over to the vacuum, and I told Phil to push it into his room. I had already prepared for this lesson by making a maze of Xs with tape on the carpet. I held his hand and demonstrated how to unroll the vacuum cord. I replaced it, and had him attempt unwinding it independently. Then, walking over to the wall outlet, I verbally prompted, "Plug it in." Motor modeling again, I showed him the motion of vacuuming by tracing the maze of Xs with the vacuum. We did two Xs together. Then I pointed to the next one and said, "Get it." He pushed the vacuum over the X. It helped to alternate between doing some together, and doing some with me gesturing or tapping his hand.

Tuesday

I said, "Phil, let's walk over to the closet to get the vacuum." He opened the door and just stood there. I got him to move again by pointing to the vacuum and saying, "Pull it out." I gestured toward his room and started to unroll the cord. I encouraged him to help by tapping his hand, as a tactile prompt, and he did. I walked over to the outlet, pointed to it, and said, "Plug it in." Again, we followed the maze of Xs on the floor to get the carpet vacuumed. He only needed me to tap his hand to start him moving or occasionally provide a verbal prompt like "keep going."

Wednesday

To get started, I told Phil to go to the closet and retrieve the vacuum. He took the vacuum out, but left it right outside the door to his room. I said to him, "Let's vacuum your room." I opened the door and said, "Inside." I walked over to the vacuum, pointed to the cord and said, "Unwind." This combination of visual and auditory prompts worked well. I only offered the verbal prompt of "plug it in," and he did. Today, I wanted to let him push the vacuum on his own as much as possible. I told him to push and follow the Xs on the floor. This verbal prompt was sufficient for him to complete the task.

Thursday

Before we started today, I removed half of the Xs from the carpet, leaving more at the beginning of his path and fading quickly. I tapped Phil's shoulder and pointed to the closet where we kept the vacuum. I said, "Open it." He opened the closet door. I took his hand, placed it on the vacuum, and pointed to his room. Moving his hand in this way provided him the kinesthetic prompt to start and continue the needed movement. After arriving in the room, he got distracted. I used a kinesthetic prompt again. I took his arm and placed his hand on the cord. I said, "Unwrap." He held the cord as I walked him over to the outlet. I said, "Plug it in." I then encouraged him to start by saying, "Go ahead."

I only used verbal prompts to keep him moving: "keep going," "missed a spot," or "finish it up."

Friday
Before I told Phil to vacuum his room, I took all the tape off the carpet. I didn't want him to become dependent on the visual prompt. Standing next to the closet where the vacuum was located, I called Phil over. I used verbal prompts: "open it," "grab the vacuum," and "in your room." I pointed to the vacuum cord and prompted: "unwrap it," "plug it in," and "push the power button." He didn't move at first, so I tapped him and said, "Go." He started off and followed the previous path of the Xs. He deviated some, but largely vacuumed the rug on his own.

Saturday
I told Phil, "You need to vacuum the carpet in your room." He seemed to not to want to move, so I went over to him and verbally prompted him by saying, "Please get up and go vacuum your room." He moved, placed the vaccum in his room, but then just stood there with the vacuum. I used a visual prompt by getting in his line of vision. I pointed to the cord on the vacuum and the plug on the wall. This helped him initiate unwrapping the cord and plugging it in. He was able to press the power button on his own and get going. A few times during the actual vacuuming, I prompted him visually by pointing to areas he had missed.

Clearing the Table

Sunday
I wanted Phil to be responsible for cleaning up his place after he had finished eating. Using a tactile prompt, I touched his hand and told him to pick up the fork and knife and place them in the middle of the plate. Then I asked him to pick up the plate using both hands and take it to the sink. I assured him that I would walk next to him in case anything fell. This combination of tactile and auditory prompts was effective.

Monday
After Phil finished his breakfast and had an empty plate, I placed a little piece of paper in the center of his empty plate. This visual prompt helped Phil know where to place his knife and fork. I requested he place his utensils on top of the piece of paper. Using a visual prompt, I physically demonstrated how to pick up the plate and said, "Take it to the sink." I walked next to him to help as a visual and kinesthetic prompt and to keep him confident in his ability to complete the task.

Tuesday

Today we worked on Phil taking his plate to the sink twice, once after breakfast and again after lunch. The repetition reinforced the process. The more he practices, the better he will be. I used visual and verbal prompts, pointing to the fork and the knife. I said, "Place them on the plate." He was able to do so. I then pointed to the sink and said, "Plate to the sink." Again, I walked beside him to give him security that if something fell, I would catch it. I also reminded him to visually attend to the plate to prevent a mistake. We repeated this process at lunch with an additional tactile prompt of tapping to help him get started.

Wednesday

Again, Phil picked up his plate after two meals. After breakfast, I motor modeled, hand-over-hand two to three times. He immediately tried independently, moving the knife and fork to the center of the plate. Prompting him after dinner, I sat in front of him and—in his field of vision—placed my fork on my plate. I did the same with my knife. This visual prompt helped him to be able to move his fork and knife to his plate. I followed up with a combination of auditory and visual prompts. I said, "Look at my hands." I grabbed the plate with two hands and carried it to the sink. He watched and did the same. I reminded him to take his time on the way there.

Thursday

Today, I aimed at having him clear his plate after each meal. I tried to use the least number of verbal prompts possible, so I pointed to Phil's fork and knife and then to the middle of the plate. I provided this visual prompt three times before he was able to initiate moving his utensils to his plate. Next, I pointed to the sink and said, "Plate to the sink." The verbal prompt was sufficient. For other meals, I used the same prompts, though I only had to visually prompt once.

Friday

Using a tactile prompt, I touched Phil's arms and told him to pick up the fork and the knife and place them in the center of the plate. Following that, I placed his hands on the edges of the plate and prompted with "grasp" and "pick it up." Pointing to the sink, I said, "Plate to the sink." The tactile and auditory prompts helped Phil succeed.

Saturday

After breakfast, Phil walked away from the table. I verbally prompted by saying, "If you are done, where does your plate go?" He looked at me, and I pointed to the sink. He responded by picking up his plate up and putting it in the sink. For lunch and dinner today, he took his plate to the sink without any prompts. I did remind him once to watch where he was going.

Wiping Table

Sunday

To get Phil started, I placed a damp kitchen rag on the tabletop and told him we would wipe down the table. I began by using motor modeling, hand-over-hand two to three times. He immediately tried this independently, making circular motions with the rag. Together, we moved around the table to wipe it clean. We practiced twice together, and then he wiped the table on his own. To help him persist, I used a verbal prompt, "Keep going."

Monday

After lunch, I placed the damp rag on the table again. However, this time I used visual and verbal prompts. I pointed to the table and said, "Wipe." When Phil stopped or paused, I tapped the table to help him finish.

Tuesday

Once dinner was over and the table was cleared, I took small pieces of tape and made a trail around the table indicating where I wanted him to wipe. I called him over to the sink and pointed to the rag, "Grab it," I said. I had him follow me to the table. Hand-over-hand two to three times, I had him follow the visual prompts of tape to wipe the whole surface. After the second time of me directing him through the tape, he wanted to do it on his own. I watched and waited, thrilled that he did not need additional prompts to complete that task.

Wednesday

"Phil, please go get the rag by the sink," I told him. I used a visual prompt by pointing to the rag, and he grabbed it. I used pieces of tape on the table surface as a visual prompt again and pointed to the spots he missed. Simply using visual prompts was effective today.

Thursday

Phil and I stood in front of the sink, and I pointed to the rag. He didn't move. I used a tactile prompt by placing his hand on top of the rag. I said, "Grab it." Using a visual prompt, I pointed to the table and said, "Wipe it." Today he was able to wipe well with this combination of prompts.

Friday

Today we practiced wiping the table after each meal: breakfast, lunch, and dinner. While I sat at the table, I pointed to the rag and said, "Grab it." Then I said, "Wipe it." After two of the three meals, he just placed the rag on the table and sat down. In those instances, I moved his hand toward the rag, a kinesthetic prompt, to start him moving. He began wiping, but needed some motor modeling. At dinner, I added the tape back in to help him succeed.

Saturday

Having Phil wipe the table three times daily repeatedly exposed him to the process that helped him improve. Today after breakfast, I used just one verbal prompt; I said, "Wipe the table." He went to the sink, got the rag, and wiped the table. At lunch, I needed to supply a bit more prompting. After lunch, I pointed to the rag and he got it. However, he needed a tactile prompt of me tapping his hand to get the circular motion going. At dinner, I brought the rag to the table, pointed to it, and he immediately began wiping.

Support and Practice are Essential

When you develop motor skills, it is important to remember that your child's success drives the process. For this reason, it is likely you will not teach all of these skills at the same time. Your child's needs vary each day. Your response— the support you provide that day—will change. Whenever you add to a skill or change the environment in which it is performed, you add difficulty. Expect your child to need more support in these times. Even slight changes like another person being present can alter the environment and impact performance.

Consistency requires that you prioritize what you want to teach, and schedule those top priority lessons into your day. If you are interested in a list of skills, please refer to the appendix for ideas. Don't overwhelm yourself or your child, though; starting small is fine. In our experience, we discovered that the quality of the lessons coupled with time for ample practice was more effective than aiming for greater quantity. Starting a process focused on quality lessons, and giving those lesson priority in our daily schedule, ultimately made the biggest difference in improving Phil's motor capabilities.

CHAPTER 7

SOCIALIZATION

―――――――――――――――――――――

A knock at the front door signals visitors. Phil runs to open it. In walks a neighbor mom and her children, welcome playmates for my kids. Immediately, the children scatter in a rush of chatter and laughter. A boy follows Phil into the living room where Phil has spread snap circuits out on the table. The boys survey the pieces briefly, sit down and set to work. In no time, the sounds of alarms buzzing and fans whirring come to life as the boys complete their projects. The lack of verbal exchange between the two does not hinder the use of their hands to create something interesting . . . nor does it diminish their appreciation for each other's work.

―――――――――――

W hen we first received Phil's diagnosis, I wondered how it would impact his socialization with family and friends. Relationships are such a big part of life; they make the daily grind worthwhile. What would relationships look like for Phil if he could not verbally express himself? Yes, this presented a limitation, but talking is not the only way of interacting. I soon realized that motor skills play a large role in relationship building and inclusion.

When Phil's motor skills were severely limited, he had few options. Unable to verbally or physically participate, he'd simply walk around in endless circles and spin toys. His limitations made me think about children in general, their interests and the motor skills they use across all stages of development. I also thought about the importance for Phil to have a childhood full of memories made with friends and family, a childhood comprised of rich experiences and rewarding relationships that encompassed more than therapy.

I made a list of activities that would provide Phil opportunities to socialize and imagined the motor skills they required. The list included air hockey, baseball, playing catch, playing board games, and coloring. I wanted to start out with something simple and fun. At the suggestion of a wonderful occupational therapist, we cut a pool noodle in half to use as a bat and paired it with a balloon for a ball. The soft equipment eliminated worries about Phil hurting himself or others. Also, the balloon is much slower than a regular ball, a helpful dynamic when it came to teaching. All three of my children enjoyed the balloon and noodle variation of baseball.

Two Dimensional Socialization Motor Skills

Our journey developing social motor skills started in the two-dimensional realm, where Phil is most comfortable. This included lessons in setting up puzzles, assembling snap circuits, and playing board games. The transition from pointing at letter board level to the tabletop enters the three-dimensional plane and requires Phil's eyes to learn a new field of intentional vision. Once he was able to focus on the tabletop, we worked on getting his hands to join his eyes to accomplish moving the pieces needed to complete an activity.

Beginning in the two-dimensional plane preserved Phil's dignity and fueled his confidence. I presented new skills in that familiar area where his eyes and hands had already functioned together successfully many times. I introduced only one new element—replacing the letter board with a game. Phil's self-esteem remained intact as he diversified his skills in a comfortable place. We then transitioned from "doing" the new skills at letter board level to doing the same motor movement on the tabletop. As ever, I initiated prompts to support that transition.

Phil was motivated to learn new motor skills for socialization because he has more of a fun, jokester personality. Although he tolerates what I require of him in terms of schoolwork, like many ten-year-olds, he prefers entertainment. He craves inclusion and to be part of the laughter with friends and family. Watching him participate in Scrabble at Christmas was like a dream; his ability to be part of our traditions always brings tears to my eyes. Moments like these remind me the worth of every minute we dedicate to learning and practice.

Reflect on activities your child shares with family and friends. What social motor skills would enhance those experiences? What lessons might enrich that engagement? Allow yourself to dream for a moment what fuller participation and inclusion would look like. Imagine how your child would feel and how you would feel. Imagine the pride and joy you would share afterward, knowing what it took to get there.

Puzzles

Puzzling is a motor skill that ages beautifully. A preschool child works puzzles just as his elderly great grandmother works puzzles. This skill never ages and can be enjoyed with family and friends easily.

Phil initially had trouble looking at the tabletop, a visual tolerance that required practice. So we started with a two-piece paper puzzle on a clipboard at letter board level. I had him point to each piece of the puzzle. Then I moved the pieces to the edge of the clipboard and put a bit of tape in the middle where each piece should go. I requested he point to one puzzle piece, grab it, and place it on the correct piece of tape. He did this and then pointed, grabbed, and placed the second piece as well.

Prompting is essential to this two-dimensional puzzling. I used auditory prompts like asking Phil to look at the clipboard puzzle; I used directional prompts like "up" and "down," and encouraging prompts like "keep going." For visual prompts, you can place the clipboard where your child usually spells or put it in her line of vision and lower it to letter board level. You might try tactile prompts like placing tape where the puzzle pieces go or placing a rolled piece of tape on each puzzle piece to make it easier for your child to grab. You can also use kinesthetic prompts by moving your child's hand to start movement, or demonstrating the action of the movement from piece to puzzle before touching it. Motor modeling is also very helpful. Try placing your hand over your child's hand two to three times, and then allow her to try immediately after.

We increased the paper puzzle to four or six pieces over time on the clipboard. Then, we worked on the tabletop. Start with a puzzle your child has already done on the clipboard, as feeling successful is important. Pointing first to the pieces on the clipboard, then pointing to them on the tabletop helps to bridge between the two-dimensional and three-dimensional realms. Grabbing moves into the three-dimensional world, so remember to increase your prompts the first few times. Adding visual prompts like a sticker or tactile prompts like tape where the puzzle piece needs to go can be useful also. Remember to eliminate prompts over time. Experiment using fewer prompts and varying the prompts to avoid dependency and continue motor growth.

Also, consider how much the eyes and hands have to work together. It was a challenge for Phil to use both together. To accommodate his tolerance, we started slowly, working only a minute or two each day and then increasing incrementally. He would rub his eyes or get hyper when he fatigue set in. I had to approach his visual abilities like an atrophied muscle; we built endurance intentionally, but slowly and surely.

Once Phil could do a ten-piece puzzle, jumping to 24 pieces only involved adding more prompts for a period of time. Buying 24-piece puzzles at the dollar store was an economical way to get a variety of puzzles. I reminded Phil that the designs may not be ones he liked, but in time, once we reach 100 pieces and beyond, he would have many more choices. Phil has since chosen many Harry Potter puzzles, as he is a huge fan.

Snap Circuits

Phil fell in love with Snap Circuits when my sister gifted them to his younger sister. Snap Circuit building kits by Elenco allow children to build electronic circuit experiments that make lights turn on, alarms blare, fans spin, etc. The pieces are solid, and all the experiments are constructed on a hard plastic grid. The directions are colorful and easy to follow. Our whole family has come to enjoy Snap Circuits, including my four-year-old, who assembles them with just a little help.

Initially, as I saw Phil watching his younger sister assemble circuit projects, I felt unsure of his ability to do this too. The process involved handling many unique parts in various sequences. I have learned, however, that my hesitations about what Phil can or cannot do limit his potential. It helped when I recalled the success we had already achieved developing his motor skills on many fronts. I knew that Phil performed well in a two-dimensional setting at letter board level, so that would be the best place to start with Snap Circuits.

I picked up the hard plastic grid with a battery pack on it and all of the pieces assembled except the one that would finish the circuit. Once completed, this configuration would turn on a little light. I pointed to the missing piece on the table and instructed Phil to point to it also. Then I asked him to grab it, and I gestured toward the spot it needed to go on the grid in my hands. He placed it, and together we snapped it into place. I took his hand and flicked the switch. The light came on, and he was delighted.

We made this same experiment several times over the next few days. Each time, I left out more pieces. I showed him the instructions in his visual field.

I gave him two choices on the tabletop to decide which piece he needed next. Between each placement, we pointed to the instructions and back to the pieces. This bridged our work with each piece from the two-dimensional to the three-dimensional realm. Over time, I put the instructions on the tabletop and prompted for his eyes to look at them. I also laid three or more pieces on the table for him to find what he needed among them.

After Phil was able to do several experiments with me holding the hard plastic grid at letter board level, I lowered it to the table. We went back to the very first simple experiment we did together, switching on the light. With prompts and some motor modeling, Phil worked with the pieces on the tabletop. I took his hand and had him place the first piece with me. For the next piece, I verbally prompted him, saying, "Grab it." I pointed (a visual prompt) to the place where it belonged on the structure. I varied my prompts between gestures and verbal directions or affirmations to continue. When he struggled to find the next piece amid many, I narrowed it down to two or three choices. We continued practicing a few different projects with my prompting as needed.

As time passed, the prompts lessened. I usually waited nearby to see what he would do next. If he froze or misplaced something, I would prompt; if not, I would just watch. Eventually I was simply a spectator for the circuit experiments, which he had practiced. Each new experiment builds in complexity and presents different challenges. I would, at times, take his hands and guide an action, then give him a turn. Other times, to get his body moving, I just said, "look again" or "keep at it." Once Phil had finished the projects in the first Snap Circuits set, he wanted to take on more and more challenging experiments. We have since purchased additional sets for birthdays and Christmas.

When other kids come over to play, Phil can show them how to assemble the experiments. His sense of accomplishment as he shows a friend is heartwarming. I treasure the day he took his Snap Circuits for his "how to" presentation to our homeschool group. He demonstrated an experiment, which did not require verbal explanation. He answered his peers' questions via spelling on his letter board. His classmates were intrigued, and he beamed with pride as he returned to his seat.

Air Hockey

This was one of the first games that I taught Phil. Since he favors kinesthetic learning, I thought he would enjoy the movement air hockey allowed. We started with a crumpled piece of paper that we flattened into a disk-like shape for the puck. Then we crumpled another paper, but gave it a handle-like shape and a flat bottom for the mallet. Using our paper puck and mallet on the tabletop, I motor modeled swinging movements, hand-over-hand two or three times. I then immediately let him try moving the mallet side-to-side and forward and backward independently.

We practiced daily, holding and moving the mallet in different directions. I placed the puck in front of the mallet and motor modeled how to push with it. The puck would slide across the tabletop. Together, we rolled two cylinders and taped them into a goal shape on the other side of the table. Sitting down together, I motor modeled hitting the puck through the goal. Then using verbal prompts and gestures, I encouraged him to do it several times. When he faltered, I motor modeled again, always supporting him to be successful. As the parent or caregiver working simultaneously on developing motor skills and building confidence, you engage in a delicate dance between more prompts and fewer prompts.

Eventually, Phil needed only a few prompts to play air hockey on the tabletop with a paper puck and mallet. We then bought an air hockey table. Playing on the air hockey table dramatically changed the environment and the game pieces. To support Phil in this transition, we returned to me motor modeling the movements. We practiced several minutes each day with me at this side. Next, I moved to the other side of the table to be his opponent. This was another change, so I added prompts that would help him succeed and then removed the prompts over time. Keep in mind, changing opponents adds challenge, and challenges often require additional prompts. Also, anticipate the need to add prompts when your child plays games with a new person.

Playing Catch

When I found out I was pregnant with Phil, I thought about all the things we would do together as a family over the years. My husband is a huge St. Louis Cardinals fan, so I imagined father and child playing catch in the yard and watching games on the TV. Learning to play catch did indeed enrich Phil by opening the door for him to greater socialization. He plays catch now with his friends and family. Watching him play catch with his younger brother warms my heart every time; I like that they can share in a brief game together. Lately, he has played a few games of catch with his grandfather, another great opportunity to connect with family.

Phil previously enjoyed throwing, but mostly at random or as hard as he could. Teaching him to control his throw, I had to consider safety first and how to turn his impulse into functional throwing. I chose to start with a balloon, as it does not go very far regardless of how hard you throw it. I put a large X with tape on the wall. I handed him the balloon and motor modeled throwing, hand-over-hand two to three times. He then tired independently. We practiced a little each day and made a game of counting how many times we hit the target.

When his throwing improved, I changed the X to a smiley face made of tape and bought a large inflatable bouncy ball from the grocery store. Using this new ball, I returned to motor modeling to give him the feel of how hard to throw the ball. I used verbal prompts and gestures (a visual prompt, that reminded him when to release and also helped him reduce the force). Next, we used a whiffle ball in our practice throwing at the target. As needed, I executed a throwing action next to Phil (a visual prompt), or tapped (a tactile prompt) to help him get started.

After Phil was able to throw with few prompts, I stood in front of him and verbally prompted him to throw the ball to me. I needed to remind him to look at me prior to throwing and sometimes gesture to get him to focus on where he was throwing. I handed him the ball back each time. We practiced for a couple minutes each day. We followed this same process for learning to catch.

Catching uses a combination of skills; it involves eyes to track and the body to move. I started by showing Phil how to hold his arms out and move them from side to side and up and down. This required motor modeling, hand-over-hand two to three times, followed by Phil trying independently. I took his arms in mine and said, "up," moving them up; or "down," moving them down; or "side to side," moving them from side-to-side. After each instruction, he practiced the appropriate movement. We practiced this until he could initiate moving in the appropriate direction at the prompt of a gesture or hearing the words "up," "down," or "side to side."

Beginning with a balloon was great, because I could throw it up high or directly at Phil, giving him time to adapt to the balloon's slow movement. Gesturing, tapping his arm, or verbally reminding him to extend his arms were all helpful prompts in getting him positioned to catch the balloon. We practiced this for a couple of minutes each day until he only required a few reminder prompts here and there.

It was lots of fun once we could play back and forth. Then we introduced playing catch with others, a change in environment that added an element of challenge. It took about a month or so for Phil to achieve the same level of ease playing with another person as he experienced when he played with me. In time, Phil's ability to play catch solidified bonds and brought joy to our entire family.

Board Game: Sorry

I was raised in a family that played board games. I have so many great memories of family and friends laughing and joking around a game table. To me, the dream of Phil participating in games was worth pursuing. We began with the game Sorry. I prepared by identifying the motor skills playing Sorry required. These included grabbing a card from a pile, turning it over, and moving a pawn as needed. Phil would need visual tolerance to look at the board and find the stack of cards; he would need visual tolerance as well to find the pawn to move.

I started by leading a brief RPM lesson explaining the rules of the game. Then, with an empty game board on the tabletop, I instructed him to point to the four corners of the board. I motor modeled, hand-over-hand two to three times indicating the four corners. Phil immediately tried independently. This familiarized Phil with how far he would need to reach to move his pawn. In Sorry, the deck of cards is at the center of the game board, so we practiced pointing to this location also. When needed, I lifted the game board to letter board level and had Phil point to the card area. I then returned the board to the table and had him point to it again.

In time, we added the deck of cards and a pawn. I requested he point to the deck of cards and motor modeled picking up a card, placing it in his visual field, and looking at the words on the card. Together, we read the card and placed it on the discard pile. We did this two to three times together. I then used verbal prompts and gestures for him to attempt it independently. On the third card draw, we worked together, hand-over-hand, to move the pawn the number of spaces it stated. On the next card draw, I pointed to the pawn and verbally encouraged him to start moving spaces, counting with him, and prompting him with a tap to stop when needed.

I used various prompts—auditory, visual, tactile and kinesthetic—to help Phil initiate actions like draw a card, read it, discard it, and move the pawn. My motor modeling helped him get a feel for the motion needed to complete the task. I used visual prompts like moving the pawn or gesturing in the Phil's visual field. I used auditory prompts like murmuring, singing or saying a word. I used tactile prompts like tape on the game board or tapping Phil's hands to get them initiated. I used kinesthetic prompts like moving Phil's hands or arms to get them started. Combining prompts and changing volume or pressure opened the door to a wide variety of prompts and reduces dependence on only one prompt.

Joining and Bonding

Like me, Phil wants to be involved in relationships with friends and family. Using a letter board can be taxing and does not provide inclusion across multiple settings. His ability to play games, engage in hobbies, and bond with others enriches his life. While the motor skills these activities require take time, dedication, and practice; the results are worth it. Fun with family and friends not only improves his experiences now, it creates a bank of pleasant memories. Someday in the future, he too may relish laughter around a game table or the joy of a backyard game of catch.

CHAPTER 8

MOTOR AND FITNESS

The music booms as Philip and I jump up and step down, jump up and step down. We complete the set of box jumps and move to the wall to begin our squats. Hands up, palms flat against the wall we hinge at the hips and begin counting. Twenty minutes later, we lie on the floor, sweat dripping from our brows in a welcome calm that follows all the exertion. Philip and I are fitter, stronger, and impressed with the progress our bodies have made as we diversify our movement and develop more and more command over our newly found muscles.

M y personal fitness journey began in response to a need: I needed to relieve the stress of sleepless nights, sensory meltdowns, and the drain of emotional energy that came with caring for three young children, educating them, and resolving tantrums and arguments. By the end of the day, I was more than mentally and physically exhausted; I was emotionally spent. I found that physical exercise significantly reduced my anxiety and regulated my mood. The improvements I experienced made me wonder if Phil might benefit from exercise, too.

At first, getting Phil to exercise seemed counterintuitive. After all, he was constantly moving and his build was on the lean side. But after watching him for a few days, I noticed that he mostly used his legs. He was in motion, but only running and jumping. As for his upper body, he typically lifted nothing more than small, lightweight objects.

When Phil rested, he preferred leaning against a wall as he sat, or lying on the floor. At first, I thought he just liked the feeling of support, but when I coaxed him to try one sit up, I realized he had little core strength. It dawned on me how disjointed his body must feel: strong and tight leg muscles in need of stretching, and weak muscles everywhere else. Developing motor skills for exercise would create the balance he needed to be healthy; it would also improve the connection between his brain and body.

Without knowing where to start, I simply chose activities that focused on weak muscles, and aimed at stretching the kinks out of his overworked legs. He fought me tooth and nail with any kind of stretching. His legs were so tight, he could not even sit at a ninety-degree angle. When I stretch, I think of it as good pain; I am not sure how he registers it, but he is not a fan. Despite his resistance, I daily stretched his legs for a couple of minutes, either hand-over-hand or stretching next to him as a visual prompt, encouraging him verbally.

In addition to the stretches, we did crunches, supine stretches, leg raises, and wheelbarrow walking. We used motor modeling for all, hand-over-hand two to three times, followed by his immediate independent attempt. At first, he ran away constantly. A few months passed before he settled in. Gradually, he required fewer prompts. It helped to have someone next to him doing the exercise with him, both as a visual prompt and for the social aspect of a workout partner. Around the three-month mark, he was able to sit at a ninety-degree angle with his legs fully flat to the ground.

Choosing exercises for Phil was not my forte. I am not well versed in fitness, so I read about the impact of fitness on the body and the best kinds of exercise. John Ratey's book *Spark: The Revolutionary New Science of Exercise and the Brain* (Little, Brown and Company, 2013) was enlightening. He touched on all the neurological effects of working out, including better academic scores, regulated mood and hormones, and improved self-esteem. I saw value in developing Phil's brain in this way and in the potential social implications of having a workout buddy. I also re-read Ido Kedar's book *Ido in Autismland* (Sharon Kedar: 2012) and thankfully found Mike Ramirez, who became Phil's coach.

Reaching out to Mike was helpful, as he had all the knowledge I lacked. After talking with him, I knew that our home program would improve. Mike founded

Special-Fit, which focuses on fitness for persons challenged with disabilities including autism. He comes from a CrossFit foundation and framework. The application of his knowledge for our children has made fitness available regardless of diagnosis. I attended Mike's training and consulted with him to start workouts at home with Phil.

The workouts were intense, and we experienced a steep learning curve. I had to figure out how to engage Phil in exercise when he preferred running away, giving me dead weight, or laughing excessively. Since the activities were new, it felt like we were starting all over. As with other times when I taught Phil new motor movements, it felt like we were going backwards for the first few weeks. Sheer determination kept me engaging him. Without fail, I motor modeled and prompted Phil through three workouts each week. I also participated in monthly consultations. After several months, an exercise regimen started to come together. Phil became more compliant and the exercises became more fluid.

Understanding the progression of the exercises helped me introduce and teach them to Phil. Special-Fit features variety; no two workouts are the same. This diversity helped us steer clear of challenges we typically faced with "routine," given Phil's obsessive compulsive tendencies.

Our exercise regimen was not about perfection as much as it was about practicing new movements. It integrated a few dozen exercises in different orders and variations. I've listed a few of them below, together with how we used motor modeling and prompting to help Phil succeed.

Squats

Squats are deceptively complex, involving balance, strength and motion. I wanted Phil was to use good form that prevented injury, strengthened muscles, and developed coordination. The first step to a squat is to have your feet about shoulder width apart. Then pull your bottom back and hinge at the hips.

On the days when squats felt especially tough, I started with motor modeling. Hand-over-hand, I guided Phil through the movement two to three times; then Phil tried independently. Motor modeling seemed to help his brain and body connect and work together more fully. To achieve the downward motion of the squat, he responded best to me holding his hands and pulling down. If this did not get him to hinge at the hips, I would have another person grab his hips. Keeping Phil's hands up in my hands and having a helper guide his hips gave Phil a feel for the whole motion. We would just keep moving Phil until he got a feel for it. If you do not have a helper, start with the hips and go from there.

It also helped to place a chair behind Phil, should he lose balance and end up sitting. For a visual prompt, I placed masking tape on the floor for his feet and on the chair where his bottom needed to land. We made sure to master these steps and gradually reduce the number of needed prompts before moving on to movements that completed the squat.

Once Phil regularly got to the place where he hinged at the hips, I had him make sure his spine was neutral and his chest was "big," like Superman. I placed my hands on his chest and back showing him how his back should be aligned. I used the verbal prompt, "hinge" to get him to move down. We did this two to three times, then I let go of his chest and back and encouraged him to "hinge" without my hands. He was able to get a feel for it with support before he tried the movement independently.

Using verbal prompts like "big" to prevent his chest from caving, in combination with "hinge," helped him maintain correct posture, while attempting to squat. When he first learned the movement, I assured him it was fine for him to sit directly down on the chair. In time I moved the chair back so his bottom touched only the edge, versus actually sitting. The tactile prompt of feeling the edge helped him know when to go back up. When I executed the squat in front of or beside Phil, I provided a helpful visual prompt. My joining in also encouraged him by reminding him he was not working out alone.

While practicing squats daily, I used the auditory prompts of "hinge," "big," or "bottom back." I used the visual prompts of me demonstrating the movement, an X on the floor, and gesturing to help Phil initiate or keep good form. Tactile prompts included tapping his hips to assist in that movement, or placing a piece of tape or sticker on his hands to remind him to keep them off his knees. When it seemed like he was unable to start moving, I would use the kinesthetic prompt of starting to move his body for just a second, like a little push in the right direction. Using these prompts one at a time or together helped him succeed; varying the prompts prevented prompt dependency. It also helped me as a teacher to remember that our program was not about perfection as much as it was about practicing new movements.

Pull-Ups

As I planned exercises for Phil, preventing injuries remained a top priority. A fall would not only bring him pain, but it would damage his confidence and erode self-trust. In the case of pull-ups, this meant trusting his hands. As Phil's teacher, I needed to remember that pull-ups involve grabbing and releasing, two separate motor skills. I also needed to remember that though Phil might focus on keeping his hands grasping, they might not obey. Practice was essential to improving the connection between his brain and his body, which led to trust in his hands.

We started with Phil holding onto a pull-up bar with his arms fully extended, but his feet on the floor or a chair. He was hanging, but without the added potential of falling. First he hung for a few seconds with his feet still on the ground. In time, we built up to 30 seconds. Next, we placed the bar a bit higher, so his feet would be just off the ground; if he fell he would be safe. Once he sustained 30 seconds with his feet off the ground, we worked on him pulling up to put his shoulders back in the sockets. To show him the action, I lifted him slightly, saying "shoulders in." This guidance and direction helped him get a feel for it. When I let him try independently I gestured and said, "shoulders in." As needed, I would move him again, motor modeling, or tapping near his shoulders, or visually modeling my request in front of him.

Eventually, Phil was able to put his shoulders in the sockets while hanging 10 times. Next, I put a stretchy exercise band around the bar and under his feet. This gave him pressure from under his feet, and I lifted him up to a full pull-up motion. I moved him two or three times, then requested, "up" while gesturing. He was able to move a little. I moved him again, and he tried again. We alternated between help with one pull-up and independence on the next. Over the course of several weeks, he was pulling higher each time. The day all of the parts came together, he was thrilled. He stepped down from the pull-up bar full of pride and elated to be a strong boy.

Once Phil was easily executing pull-ups with few or no prompts, we worked on removing the exercise band. He expressed concerns about this change by running away, whining while hanging, and trying to put the exercise band back on the pull-up bar. We landed on a compromise. I would use the band for two pull-ups; then I would use my hands under his feet for two pull-ups. This seemed to help, and in time, his confidence grew. The tactile prompt of touching his feet to help him start the action was the final step to full independence. Learning the pull-up took Phil over a full year. There are still days where he insists on the band. Perhaps he does not trust his hands that day, or wants the reassurance for some other reason.

Keep in mind the importance of encouraging your child. In our house, we avoid phrases like "good job" because our goal is progress, not perfection. I never want my child's self esteem to be based on his ability to perform, but rather on his grit to keep at it. And honestly, there are days when the brain isn't a friend to his hands. On those days, we take steps back. Sometimes continual growth requires backing up and trying again. Saying things like, "I know it is tough, but you've got this," "one more," or "nice form" help acknowledge your child's efforts. Meet your child where he is today. If motor modeling works best today, do that. If it seems your child is not visually engaged, rely more on auditory prompts like "grab it," "hold it," and "up." Tactile prompts of tapping parts of the body or placing tape on joints can help initiate the desired movement. Modeling—a visual prompt—in front of or beside him can help sustain movement. If modeling doesn't work one day, combine prompts or try different ones.

Sit-Ups

Core strength was an issue for Phil, and we wanted to tackle it. Sit-ups are great for core strength. I laid him down, bent his legs, and grabbed his arms, pulling his trunk toward his knees. Still holding his arms, I gently lowered him toward the ground. I did not want him to bang his head on the way down, as it requires core strength to lay back down with ease. For two to three sit-ups I would grab his arms saying "up" and "down" moving him through the action. On the third time, I gestured and said "up" and "down." He moved slightly off the ground. I persisted and grabbed his arms assisting him with two more sit-ups. Again, I gestured and verbally prompted him. This time he moved up halfway toward his knees.

When Phil tries independently, any movement at all is a start worth celebrating. The more we practiced, the more he was able to get his body moving. We took the small victories; in time a full sit-up emerged. Our sit-up journey took several months. Phil learned not just the motor action of sitting up, but he also developed muscle mass and strength.

Running

Cardio exercise is great for fitness and heart health. While that sounds nice, getting Phil to run was like pulling a seventy-pound weight. He refused to move beyond a quick walk. He would yank me backwards and complain profusely. Getting him on a treadmill was a lifesaver. The moving track did not require him to initiate the movement, and he could not randomly stop. We worked on walking a mile and progressed to running part of it. The treadmill seemed to calm him on a tough day, and his sleep improved. However, running outside presented other challenges.

I tried again to get him to run outside. The challenge I faced was that he would run away from me rather than run with me. He failed to stop when I asked him to stop. Like all children, Phil is impulsive. Without learning how to control his impulses, the impulses would take over. Starting and stopping are motor skills that help Phil control his impulses. I explained to him that we needed to work on starting and stopping intentionally. We decided to take ten steps and stop. Practicing intentional stops this way helped curb his impulses. Eventually we varied the steps between our intentional stops. It helped when I said, "stop," touched his arm, gestured, or pushed him gently. Sometimes he needed a combination of prompts to help him succeed.

Starting and stopping are not skills that developed easily or quickly. We worked on them any time we were out doing errands, or going for a walk, or running in the evening. In the house, we worked on walking from one room to another. On different days he needed different prompts. Sometimes a gesture was enough; other times he needed a tap and verbal reminder. Consistent practice paid off. After about 18 months, Phil was able to start and stop with few or no prompts.

Free Time

Life is full of time. Typically, we divide our time between work, home, and leisure activities. Phil's schooling, chores, and hobbies only required so much of his time. The ability to use motor skills for fitness provided him something else to do in his free time. He deserves to be healthy; he benefits from exercise that reduces stress, helps him regulate his emotions, and makes him strong. He enjoys knowing he is strong and capable. The idea of personal strength makes him proud. I find that being fit contributes to my wellbeing and helps me be a better wife, mother, and friend. I want the same for Phil—to be a strong contributor to our family and community. Dedicating time to developing his strength is time well spent.

CHAPTER 9

HINDSIGHT FOR SUCCESS

Climbing into bed, I lay my head down and reflect on the day—the motor skills Phil worked on, what went well, what I would like to try tomorrow, and what needs to be edited out altogether. I choose not to dwell on guilt for falling short of perfection. I am content. Each day we tackle motor challenges with fervor. We have seen the small victories mount into to something big. We have faith that more victories will come. I have no clue where Phil and I will be four years from now, but I know that we will have grown for the better.

After almost four years implementing RPM in countless ways beyond the letter board, I have learned many things about my role as Phil's primary caregiver. I am the dreamer, the planner, the goal setter, and the daily driver of disciplined practice. I channel new discoveries into our family life—insights about self-care, tolerance, scheduling, precautions and more. I have learned that consistency is essential for Phil and me to thrive; I am the "consistency facilitator." As a momma, if I sink, the whole ship goes down. Striving for stability requires intentionality on my part.

A dear friend and I sometimes chat about our lives with our RPM boys. We talk about the hard things and the wonderful things, about the silly things and the annoying things. Often we talk about how we want to have more balance. We actively discuss self-care—preventing burnout, taking time to rebuild ourselves, and doing the same for our children. We agree that in the day-to-day, it's sometimes easy to lose sight of this truth.

For me, the first step to creating balance is self-care. This means setting healthy habits for myself. I will admit that I often sacrifice sleep to do things I want to do, like read a book or go for a walk. If I do not take times to refresh and renew, my ability to be present and patient with my family diminishes. Often my response to my spouse and children reveal deficiencies in my self-care.

I find respite and relaxation are essential to keep me in a good mindset. It took me a few years to realize that TV does not relax me. I discovered reading a book helps me unwind significantly more. Also, going for walks, swimming, and weight training help. Yoga has impacted my relaxation the most. I noticed that I do not breathe enough; adding yoga required me to take time to breathe, bringing me back to a calm baseline.

Aside from daily yoga, I have found it important to eat healthy and go out on a date with my spouse or friends every couple of weeks. I have several friends who do not have special needs children, and these relationships remind me that there is more to life than therapies and the challenges of that particular week. Try out different activities to find what really helps you relax and recharge. Make it a priority to do these things and remember who you were before you became absorbed in your child's needs.

Monitoring tolerance levels is key not only to Phil's growth and wellbeing, but they are key to my wellbeing too. When Phil has a hard week and resists everything, it is important for me to adjust our goals. I can only take so much of his resistance before I lose patience, and he has limits on how much of my pushing he can handle. Being aware of these limits helps me to form attainable goals for motor practice. Again, consistency is critical, focusing on quality not quantity helps. Two burnt-out people will not generate learning and growth.

When we started teaching motor skills, Phil demonstrated low tolerance for any movement other than RPM in an academic setting and his own preferred "stims"—repetitive body movements or noises that stimulate his senses. He used his body and hands in the same ways each day. Developing new motor skills required him to diversify. This introduced a plethora of new encounters with his world—new neurology, new muscle control, and new disciplines that facilitated growth and expanded his experiences. At the same time, motor skill development reduced opportunities for Phil to engage in familiar activities that he was accustomed to. Often, he was not on board with learning new things and fiercely resisted.

About one year into our dedicated development of motor skills, he seemed to realize the point of all these "new" encounters; his self-value and pride increased. As a parent, it was a tough year, and it still is tough when he resists. I have to keep my eyes on my purpose captured in my mission statement. I focus on my job as his parent to prepare him for life. All children have phases of disliking school, chores, or social activities. It is my responsibility to stick with the learning process through thick and thin because I know that Phil's motor independence leads to his best possible future.

Speaking from my experience, scheduling and tolerance go hand in hand. Setting up a schedule that provides realistic goals and flexibility for Phil and me has proven invaluable. While I love schedules, I struggle immensely with flexibility. I strive for things to go according to my plan, but this rarely happens. Learning to be flexible was and still is a journey Phil and I take together.

Three and a half years ago, I incorporated an ambitious schedule into our usual homeschool day: two academic RPM lessons per day for 20 minutes each, one self-care motor RPM lesson for 15-20 minutes, and following Phil around while reading aloud for 20 minutes. I committed to engaging Phil for one hour and 20 minutes daily even though he is typically awake 14 hours each day. This first schedule reflected my tolerance for doing academic and self-care motor lessons with him and his tolerance with me. I aimed to give Phil adequate academic and motor education, leveraging what I knew about our capacities for tolerance.

Once we both tolerated this schedule, I added more lessons about every two weeks to a month. My first addition was a second self-care RPM motor lesson for 15-20 minutes. Then I increased our read-aloud time to 20 minutes twice per day, utilizing an audiobook at times. We followed this expanded schedule for a few months before adding in some chores, like emptying the dishwasher or laying the table. These occurred within the context of "family life as usual" in our home, lasting several minutes as needed.

The following year, Phil moved from second to third grade academically, and the workload related to his studies increased. I retained the two RPM academic lessons, but increased them to 30 minutes each. I read aloud for one hour each day, split up into 20 minute segments or whatever time division worked best for that particular day. We added listening to music and videos about our academics, and expanded motor lessons to include hobbies. Each month or two we added a little more, always in five to ten minute increments.

I love routine. My ideal would be to follow the same schedule every day. But even if it were possible to follow this dream routine, it would not be best for Phil or me. There would be zero flexibility and no allowance for tolerance levels; we would grow frustrated and miss teachable moments. Flexibility keeps the door open for success. What doesn't work in one setting may work in another; what doesn't work in one sequence may work in another. Still, I struggled with how I would get things done without a firm schedule.

Being a type A personality, I brainstormed until I found a solution that provided both structure and flexibility. I made a list of all the things I wanted to accomplish in a day for Phil, including two RPM academic lessons, two RPM motor lessons and reading aloud (See the appendix for sample schedules). Laminating the list made it possible to cross things off as we went along, implementing a different order each day. Unchecked items at the end of the day served as our starting point the next day. Not everything got done every day, but hitting each area three times a week gave me a sense of progress.

Our schedule and goals have periodically changed, often in response to the circumstances life throws at us. During the school year, we accomplish more academics, and during the breaks, we focus more on motor skills. Still, we consistently keep both in our regular rotation of lessons. There will be ups and downs. There will be weeks of sickness, holidays, and other interruptions to routine. We have found that any break longer than a week causes problems when it comes to regaining tolerance. So, take a vacation, but remember to start back up when you return home.

Also, our schedule evolved as Phil mastered different motor skills and as holidays approached. Every semester, I reevaluate our list of academic and motor skills to assure it fits our needs. Sometimes I implement changes to accommodate our need for consistency, growth, and sanity. Reviewing my mission statement aids the process. Periodic review and reflection also keep me tuned to possible problems, like learned motor skills becoming repetitive behaviors that fuel Phil's obsessive compulsive tendencies.

The first time I experienced a motor skill gone awry was vacuuming. We motor modeled, practiced with prompts, and gradually reduced prompts as planned. I stood nearby at the start and eventually was able to busy myself in a different room while Phil vacuumed. Thrilled with his meaningful contribution to family life, I didn't realize he was vacuuming the rugs in exactly the same order every time. Phil developed a loop where he could only vacuum the rugs in that defined rotation, or else he would have meltdown. I quickly broke this by requiring him to start in a different location each time.

I now know that Phil can add new repetitive behaviors or get stuck in an OCD loop. Continuing to change things up is essential to keeping him using a skill functionally. The whole point of teaching motor skills is for him to be able to do more. I am now a cautious observer, taking care that he does not develop reliance on patterns, which may require reteaching.

Do you remember roller skating as a child and the acceleration that ushered in a feeling of freedom as the wind blew through your hair? Have you tried roller skating 20 years later? I did. I felt insecure and wiped out. The trajectory for Phil learning motor skills is like this. Learning and practice brings ups and downs. Some days, it feels like nothing comes together; other days we feel triumphant. Then there are all those days in between. Mastering motor skills is a journey full of bumps and valleys. Consistency is our best travel companion. It is most important to just stick with the plan and the process.

After two years of teaching motor skills, I realized that addressing new motor tasks somehow came easier. In our home, we refer to learning functional movement as the brain and body becoming better friends. Those synapses—that friendship—became evident when Phil transferred skills like pulling or grasping in different settings over the course of one month instead of many months. Each new skill strengthens his foundation. It's exciting to envision where we might be in ten or 15 years.

There is so much hope for Phil when I take time to teach him motor skills. There is hope for your child, too. Is it simple or easy? No, but it is worth it. OCD, Phil's stims, and just plain tiredness have knocked us down many times, but we have still gotten back up. The trajectory over time shows progress, even when discouragement creeps in any given day or hour. I rest my head on my pillow at the end of the day knowing that we gave it our all. Where is our final destination? I have no clue, but I will never regret providing Phil the opportunity to grow because he deserves it. Love is powerful. Let it drive you to be the best you can be for your child as you work together to prepare for the best possible future.

MOTOR SKILLS LISTS

Skills

- Eating: cutting poking
- Bathing: shampooing, soaping, drying
- Dressing: zipping, buttoning
- Toileting
- Walking
- Hand washing
- Face washing
- Teeth brushing
- Shopping: food, clothes
- Laundry: washer/dryer
- Vacuuming
- Sweeping
- Raking
- Folding laundry
- Making bed/changing sheets
- Dusting
- Moping
- Cutting: food and crafts
- Peeling
- Cooking
- Measuring
- Washing dishes
- Physical exercise
- Wipe down kitchen
- Buckle/unbuckle seat belt
- Read a map
- Handwriting
- Handling money: paying at store
- Writing checks
- Paying bills

Hobbies

- Darts
- Foosball
- Beading
- Looming
- Crocheting
- Billiards
- Swimming
- Dancing
- Color by number
- Board games
- Cross stitch
- Embroidery
- Skating
- Biking
- Scootering
- Knitting
- Lego building
- Model building
- Puzzles
- Origami
- Paper airplanes
- Reading
- Drawing
- Bowling
- Gymnastics
- Weightlifting
- Painting
- Ping pong
- Badminton
- Baseball
- Basketball
- Tennis
- Tetherball
- Piano
- Baking
- Yoyo
- Yoga
- Frisbee
- Gardening
- Hiking
- Horseback riding
- Jogging/running
- Photography
- Paintball
- Rock climbing

- Skiing
- Soccer
- Surfing

- Martial arts
- Cricket
- Hockey

- Drawing
- Crafting

Fine Motor

- Picking
- Poking
- Punching
- Pinching
- Flicking
- Touching
- Writing
- Drawing/coloring
- Pour
- Pick up
- Put down
- Scooping
- Copying
- Twisting
- Squeezing
- Tearing
- Peeling (tape off, orange)

- Buttoning
- Turning (pages in a book)
- Clapping
- Sorting (money, colors, etc.)
- Folding
- Rolling (play dough)
- Stringing
- Opening
- Texting/typing
- Zipping
- Giving
- Holding
- Separating
- Unlocking
- Spraying
- Transferring (one

hand to another)
- Crumpling
- Weaving
- Linking
- Pouring
- Stacking
- Lacing
- Transferring
- Squirting
- Placing
- Tweezing
- Cutting
- Tying
- Tracing
- Measuring
- Gluing
- Snapping
- Cracking (egg)

Gross Motor

- Pulling
- Packing
- Scrubbing
- Sweeping
- Pushing
- Walking
- Taking
- Wiping
- Showing
- Standing
- Sitting
- Throwing

- Pouring
- Stopping
- Crawling
- Jumping
- Catching
- Brushing (hair and teeth)
- Mopping
- Hopping
- Jumping
- Lifting
- Marching

- Blowing
- Swinging
- Folding
- Tiptoeing
- Kicking
- Drying
- Waving
- Giving
- Dropping
- Dragging
- Stretching
- Lifting

- Carrying/holding
- Punching/hitting
- Spraying
- Waiting
- Bouncing (ball)
- Closing
- Washing
- Rubbing
- Dusting
- Running
- Hugging
- Hammering
- Watering
- Bending
- Squatting
- Getting in/out (car, booth, bathroom)

SCHEDULE SAMPLES

Summer 2015

8:00	Breakfast - devotions
8:45	Listen to educational songs
9:00	Physical play outside or tennis
10:00	RPM Lesson 1
11:00	Workout - listen kids praise
12:00	Lunch - audiobook
1:00	RPM Lesson 2
2:00	Workout - listen kids praise
3:00	Snack - audiobook
3:30	Physical play outside - track
4:30	Fine motor/Art
5:00	Dinner - audiobook
6:15	Evening swim
7:15	Baths and relax
8:00	Bed & audiobook

Fall 2015 Motor Skill List

- Buttoning
- Ping pong
- Cutting
- Crochet
- Dish washing
- Teeth brushing
- Foosball / air hockey

Fall 2015

8:00-8:30	Listen to devotions (Bible study or reading)
8:30-9:00	RPM history
9:00-9:30	Workout

9:30-10:00	RPM motor skills
10:00-10:30	BREAK
10:30-11:30	Read aloud
11:30-12:00	RPM language arts
12:00-12:30	Workout
12:30-1:30	BREAK
1:30-2:00	RPM science
2:00-3:00	Read aloud
3:00-4:00	Outside time

Spring 2016

8:00-8:30	Listen to devotions (Bible study or reading)
8:30-9:00	RPM Math
9:00-9:30	Listen to math fact and trace maps
9:30-10:00	RPM motor skills: self-help
10:30-11:00	RPM History
11:00-12:00	Read Aloud: picture books and novels
12:00-2:00	BREAK
2:00-2:30	Workout
2:30-3:00	RPM motor skills: art
3:30-4:00	RPM science

Spring 2016 Motor Skills List

- Hand washing
- Face washing
- Dish washing
- Wipe counters / dust
- Money
- Snap circuits
- Photography
- Looming
- Peel / cut / bake
- Skateboard

Summer 2016

- Read aloud devotions (Bible together)
- Spelling: spell aloud or write/trace
- Dictation: five min RPM practice of spelling list words
- Math: RPM lesson
- Science experiment
- Copywork: tracing to practice copying from board in class
- History: RPM lesson or read aloud
- Reading: work on single words printed large

- Cooking: no bake items
- Art: bio, project, or video
- Exercise: Special-Fit and bike practice
- Language Arts/ Vocabulary: five min RPM lesson
- Bible Verse: listen six times to song
- Latin: listen six times to song
- Shower motor skills: shampooing and rinse

- Fine motor practice: cutting, crochet, and folding laundry
- Chore motor practice: pick up room, vacuum, sweep, & dust
- Music: piano practice
- History timeline: listen to song six times

Fall 2016 Motor Skill LIst

- Rake
- Cut veggies
- Sweep
- Brush teeth
- Make bed
- Tie shoes

- Dishes: wash, dry, put away
- Foosball
- Prepare snack
- Knot blanket/sewing
- Yoyo

Fall 2016

8:00-8:30	Listen to devotions (Bible readings) and trace maps
8:30-9:00	RPM math or language arts
9:00-9:30	RPM motor skills: self-help
9:30-10:00	Listen to memory work songs
10:00-10:30	Workout
10:30-11:00	RPM history or science
11:00-12:00	Read aloud
12:00-1:30	BREAK
1:30-2:00	Workout #2
2:00-2:30	Outside time
2:30-3:00	RPM motor skills: hobbies & self help

January 2017

- Make bed
- Brush teeth

- Copy work / educational songs for the week

- Breakfast chore: dishwasher or lay table
- Devotions
- Student News: CNN 10
- Spelling: listen, write or spell on letter board
- Language Arts: listen or choices
- Dictation: 5-10 words daily from a lesson
- Reading: holding book, pointing, and saying

- Workout
- Vocabulary: choices or listen
- Math: RPM
- Chores: vacuum, fold laundry, or rake
- Fine Motor
- Read Aloud / Audiobook: one hour
- Art: practice drawing
- Music: practice piano
- Ted Talk: listen to two
- Workout #2

Spring 2017

8:00-8:30	Listen to devotions and draw maps for geography
8:30-9:00	RPM lesson science or history
9:00-9:30	Motor skills #1: chores
9:30-10:00	RPM lesson math or language arts
10:00-10:30	Motor skills #2: hobbies
10:30-11:00	Special-Fit Workout
11:00-12:30	BREAK
12:30-1:00	Piano
1:00-2:00	Outside time
2:00-2:30	RPM Spelling: mini dictation or handwriting lesson
2:30-3:30	Read aloud
3:30-4:30	Play date or outside

Fall 2017 & Spring 2018

- Bible: listen
- Diagram sentences: in visual field, use choices occasionally
- Vocabulary: listen to words and definitions or use in sentence via choices
- Spelling: dictation, use in sentence, listen or write
- Writing: RPM brief lesson or formal RPM to teaching paper writing
- Memory Work: listen to each song six times while doing Lego, Snap Circuits, looming or puzzles
- Current events: watch CNN 10
- Geography: pointing or tracing
- Science: RPM or listen to read aloud

- Reading: Philip reads to me about 30 minutes
- Chores: cleaning, folding, prepping snack
- Workout: Special-Fit

- Piano: motor skill hobby
- Skateboard: motor skill hobby
- Art for Kids Hub: to practice drawing imitation

Summer 2018

- Listen to: spelling, scripture, Latin and science read aloud
- RPM: science or language arts
- Tennis
- RPM: holding board (five min)

- Read aloud novel
- RPM: history or math
- Swimming
- RPM: handwriting (five min)

BIBLIOGRAPHY

Abrahams, Jeffrey. *101 Mission Statements from Top Companies: plus Guidelines for Writing Your Own Mission Statement.* Ten Speed Press, 2007.

Jones, Laurie Beth. *The Path: Creating Your Mission Statement for Work and for Life.* Hachette Books, 2014.

Dweck, Carol S. *Mindset: The New Psychology of Success.* Robinson, 2017.

Faber, Adele, and Elaine Mazlish. *How to Talk so Kids Will Listen & Listen so Kids Will Talk.* Scribner, 1980.

Mukhopadhyay, Soma. *Understanding Autism through Rapid Prompting Method.* Outskirts Press, 2008.

Mukhopadhyay, Soma. *Developing Motor Skills for Autism Using Rapid Prompting Method: Steps to Improving Motor Function.* Outskirts Press, 2014.

Ratey, John J., and Eric Hagerman. *Spark: the Revolutionary New Science of Exercise and the Brain.* Little, Brown, 2013.

Made in the USA
Columbia, SC
24 September 2020